1930

EVOLUTION AND GENETICS

London: Humphrey Milford
Oxford University Press

EVOLUTION AND GENETICS

BY

THOMAS HUNT MORGAN

PROFESSOR OF EXPERIMENTAL ZOOLOGY
IN COLUMBIA UNIVERSITY

PRINCETON
PRINCETON UNIVERSITY PRESS
1925

Based on lectures delivered at Princeton University
Under the Louis Clark Vanuxem Foundation
February 24, March 1, 8, 15, 1916

∽

COPYRIGHT, 1916, BY PRINCETON UNIVERSITY PRESS
PUBLISHED OCTOBER, 1916, AS "A CRITIQUE OF THE THEORY OF EVOLUTION"
SECOND PRINTING, SEPTEMBER, 1917
THIRD REVISED PRINTING, FEBRUARY, 1919

∽

COPYRIGHT, 1925, BY PRINCETON UNIVERSITY PRESS
SECOND EDITION, SEPTEMBER, 1925

PRINTED AT PRINCETON UNIVERSITY PRESS, PRINCETON, N.J., U.S.A

PREFACE

THE third reprinting of the Vanuxem Lectures for 1915-16, entitled *A Critique of the Theory of Evolution,* having been exhausted, the publishers have asked for a revised edition. The revision is no less an attempt at a critique of the evolution theory than its predecessor, but, as the change in title suggests, greater attention is here paid to one of the most debated questions among evolutionists today, namely, the bearing of the recent discoveries in genetics and in mutation on the theory of evolution.

While in a general way Darwin's theory of Natural Selection is independent of the origin of the new variations that furnish it with its materials, yet the scientific formulation of the theory is intimately connected with the origin and inheritance of suitable variations. For instance, if most of the observed variability of animals and plants were due directly to the environment, and if the effects thus brought about were not inherited, such variability could no longer be appealed to as material for natural selection.

Again, if the variations that appear as mutants are always defective types, they could not, even though they are inherited, be appealed to as furnishing material for progressive evolution.

6851

v

A discussion of these two problems in their historical setting is one of the principal themes treated in the following pages.

The four original lectures (chapters) have been subdivided and enlarged into thirteen chapters. Two of these are entirely new, one dealing with the non-inheritance of acquired characters (copied with slight changes from the *Yale Review* for July 1924), the other a criticism of the evidence of human inheritance. The somewhat acrimonious discussion taking place at the present time concerning racial differences in man, a discussion in which "nature" and "nurture" are often confused, may furnish an excuse for the addition of this final chapter.

T. H. MORGAN

March 1925

CONTENTS

CHAPTER I

DIFFERENT KINDS OF EVOLUTION

WE use the word evolution in many ways—to include many different kinds of changes. There is hardly any other scientific term that is used so carelessly—to imply so much, to mean so little.

We speak of the evolution of the stars, of the evolution of the horse, of the evolution of the steam engine, as though they were all part of the same process. What have they in common? Only this, that each concerns itself with the *history* of something. When the astronomer thinks of the *evolution* of the earth, the moon, the sun and the stars, he has a picture of diffuse matter that has slowly condensed. With condensation came heat; with heat, action and reaction within the mass until the chemical substances that we know today were produced. This is the nebular hypothesis of the astronomer. The astronomer explains, or tries to explain, how this evolution took place, by an appeal to the physical processes that have been worked out in the laboratory, processes which he thinks have existed through all the eons during which this evolution was going on and which were its immediate causes.

When the biologist thinks of the evolution of animals and plants, a different picture presents itself. He thinks of series of animals that have lived in the

past (*fig.* 1) whose bones and shells have been preserved in the rocks (*fig.* 2). He thinks of these animals as having in the past given birth, through an

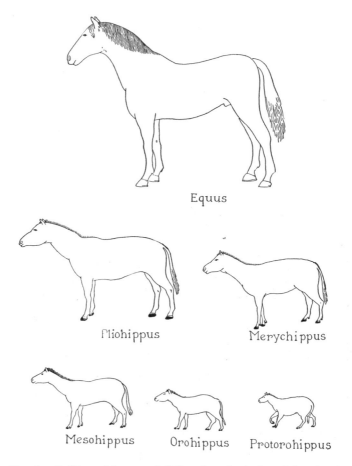

Equus

Pliohippus   Merychippus

Mesohippus   Orohippus   Protorohippus

FIG. 1.—Outline of horses of different geological periods, showing
their relative sizes and the decrease in the number of toes. (*After Lull.*)

unbroken succession of individuals, to the living in-
habitants of the earth today. He thinks that some of
the simpler types of the past have in part changed
over into the more complex forms of the present
time.

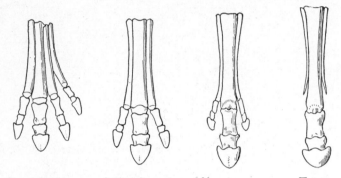

Orohippus   Miohippus   Hipparian   Equus

FIG. 2.—Forefeet of horses, showing the progressive loss of the lateral
toes. (*After Marsh, from Lull.*)

He is thinking as the historian thinks, but he runs
the risk of thinking that he is explaining evolution
when he is only describing it.

A third kind of evolution is one for which man
himself is responsible, in the sense that he has
brought it about, often with a definite end in view.

His mind has worked slowly from stage to stage.
We can often trace the history of the stages through
which his creative processes have passed. The evolution of the steam-boat, the steam engine, paintings,
clothing, instruments of agriculture, of manufac-

ture, or of warfare (*fig.* 3) illustrates the history of human progress. There is an obvious and striking similarity between the evolution of man's inventions and the evolution of the shells of molluscs and of the

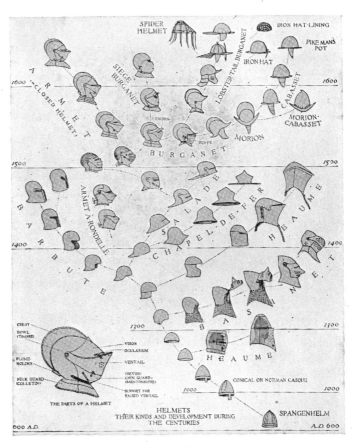

Fig. 3.—Evolution of helmets. (*After Dean.*)

bones of mammals, yet in neither case does a knowledge of the order in which these things arose explain them. If we appeal to the psychologist he will probably tell us that human inventions are either the result of happy accidents, that have led to an unforeseen, but discovered use; or else the use of the invention was foreseen. It is to the latter process more especially that the idea of *purpose* is applied. When we come to review the four great lines of evolutionary thought we shall see that this human idea of purpose recurs in many forms, suggesting that man has often tried to explain how organic evolution has taken place by an appeal to the method which he believes he makes use of himself in the inorganic world.

What, I repeat, has the evolution of the stars in common with the evolution of the horse, and what have these in common with the evolution of human inventions? Clearly no more than that from a simple beginning through a series of changes something more complex, or at least different, has come into being. To lump all these kinds of changes into one and call them evolution is only to assert that you believe in consecutive series of events (which is history) causally connected (which is science). It is the aim of science to find out *specifically* what kinds of causes were at work when the stars evolved in the sky, when the horse evolved on the earth, and the steam engine was evolved from the mind of man.

CHAPTER II

THE FOUR GREAT HISTORICAL SPECULATIONS

Looking backward over the history of the evolution theory we recognize that during the hundred and odd years that have elapsed since Buffon, there have been four main lines of *speculation* concerning evolution. We might call them the four great cosmogonies or the four modern epics of evolution.

The Environment

GEOFFROY ST. HILAIRE

About the beginning of the last century Geoffroy St. Hilaire, protégé, and in some respects a disciple, of Buffon, was interested as to how living species are related to the animals and plants that had preceded them. He was familiar with the kind of change that takes place in the embryo if it is put into new or changed surroundings, and from this knowledge he concluded that as the surface of the earth slowly changed—as the carbon dioxide contents in the air altered—as land appeared, and as marine animals left the water to inhabit it, they or their embryos responded to the new conditions and those that responded favorably gave rise to new creations. As the environment changed the fauna and flora changed— change for change. Here we have a picture of progressive evolution that carries with it an idea of mechanical necessity. If there is anything mystical or even improbable in St. Hilaire's argument it does not appear on the surface; for he did not assume that the response to the new environment was always a favorable one or, as we say, an adaptation. He expressly stated that *if* the response was unfavorable the individual or the race died out. He assumed that *sometimes* the change might be favorable, i.e., that certain species, entire groups, would respond in a direction favorable to their existence in a new environment and these would come to inherit the earth. In this sense he anticipated certain phases of the natural selection theory of Darwin, but only in part; for his picture is not one of strife within and without the species, but rather the escape of the species from the old into a new world.

If, then, we recognize the intimate bond in chemical constitution of living things and of the world in which they develop, what is there improbable in St. Hilaire's hypothesis? Why, in a word, is not more credit given to St. Hilaire in modern evolutionary thought? The reasons are to be found, I think, first, in that the evidence to which he appealed was meagre and inconclusive; and, second, in that much of his special evidence does not seem to us to be applicable. For example the monstrous forms that development often assumes in a strange environment, and with which every embryologist is only too familiar, rarely if ever furnish combinations, as he supposed, that are capable of living. On the contrary, they lead rather to the final catastrophe of the organism. And lastly, St. Hilaire's appeal to sudden and great transformations, such as crocodile's egg hatching into a bird, has exposed his view to too easy ridicule.

But when all is said, St. Hilaire's conception of evolution contains elements that form the background of our thinking today, for taken broadly, the interaction between the organism and its environment was a mechanistic conception of evolution even though the details of the theory were inadequate to establish his contention.

In our own time the French metaphysician Bergson in his *Evolution Créatrice* has proposed in mystical form a thought that has at least a superficial resemblance to St. Hilaire's conception. The response of living things is precise, exact, yet not mechanical in the sense at least in which we usually employ the word mechanical. For Bergson claims that the one chief feature of living material is that it responds favorably to the situation in which it finds itself, at least so far as lies within the possible physical limitations of its organization. Evolution has followed no preordained plan; it has had no creator; it has brought about its own creation by responding adaptively to each situation as it arose.

But note: the man of science believes that the organism responds today as it does, because at present it has a chemical and physical constitution that gives this response. We find a specific chemical composition and generally a specific physical structure already existing. We have no reason to suppose that such particular reactions would take place until a specific chemical configuration had been acquired. Where did this constitution come from? This is the question that the scientist asks himself. I suppose Bergson would have to reply that it came into existence at the moment that the first specific stimulus was applied. But if this is the answer we have passed at once from the realm of observation to the realm of fancy—to a realm that is foreign to our experience; for such a view assumes that chemical and physical reactions are guided by the needs of the organism when the reactions take place inside living beings.

Use and Disuse

FROM LAMARCK TO WEISMANN

The second of the four great historical explanations appeals to a change not immediately connected with the outer world, but to one within the organism itself.

Practice makes perfect is a familiar adage. Not only in human affairs do we find that a part through use becomes a better tool for performing its task, and through disuse degenerates; but in the field of animal behavior we find that many of the most essential types of behavior have been learned through repeated associations formed by contact with the outside.

It was not so long ago that we were taught that the instincts of animals are the inherited experience of their ancestors—lapsed intelligence was the current phrase.

Lamarck's name is always associated with the application of the theory of the inheritance of acquired characters. Darwin fully endorsed this view and made use of it as an explanation in all of his writings about animals. Today the theory has few followers amongst trained investigators, but it still has a popular vogue that is widespread.

To Weismann more than to any other single individual should be ascribed the disfavor into which this view has fallen. In a series of brilliant essays he laid bare the inadequacy of the supposed evidence on which the inheritance of acquired characters rested. Your neighbor's cat, for instance, has a short tail, and it is said that it had its tail pinched off by a closing door. In its litter of kittens one or more is found without a tail. Your neighbor believes that here is a case of cause and effect. He may even have known that the mother and grandmother of the cat had natural tails. But it has been found that short tail is a dominant character; therefore, until we know who was the father of the short-tailed kittens the accident to its mother and the normal condition of her maternal ancestry are not to the point.

Weismann appealed to common sense. He made few experiments to disprove Lamarck's hypothesis. True, he cut off the tails of some mice for a few generations but got no tailless offspring and while he gives no exact measurements with coefficients of error, he did not observe that the tails of the descendants had shortened one whit. The combs of fighting cocks and the tails of certain breeds of sheep have been cropped for many generations and the practice continues today, because sheep's tails are still long, and cocks still grow combs.

The Unfolding Principle

NÄGELI

I have ventured to put down as one of the four great historical explanations, under the heading of the unfolding principle, a conception that has taken protean forms. At one extreme it is little more than a mystic sentiment to the effect that evolution is the result of an inner driving force or principle which goes under many names such as Bildungstrieb, nisus formativus, vital force, and orthogenesis. Evolutionary thought is replete with variants of this idea, often naïvely expressed, sometimes unconsciously implied. Evolution once meant, in fact, an unfolding of what pre-existed in the egg, and the term still carries with it something of its original significance.

Nägeli's speculation may be taken as a typical

case. Nägeli thought that there exists in living material an innate power to grow and expand. He vehemently protested that he meant only a mechanical principle but, as he failed to refer such a principle to any properties of matter known to physicists and chemists, his view seems still a mysterious affirmation as difficult to understand as the facts themselves which it purports to explain.

Nägeli compared the process of evolution to the growth of a tree, whose ultimate twigs represent the living world of species. Natural selection plays only the rôle of the gardener who prunes the tree into this or that shape but who has himself *produced* nothing. As an imaginative figure of speech Nägeli's comparison of the tree might even today seem to hold if we substituted propagation and variation for "growth," but although we know so little about what causes variation there is no reason for supposing it to be due to an inner vague impulse.

In his recent presidential address before the British Association, Bateson has inverted this idea. I suspect that his effort was intended as little more than a *tour de force*. He claims for it no more than that it is a possible line of speculation. Perhaps he thought the time had come to give a shock to our too confident views concerning evolution. Be this as it may, he has invented a striking paradox. Evolution has taken place through the steady loss of inhibiting

factors. Living matter was stopped down, so to
speak, at the beginning of the world. As the stops
are lost, new things emerge. The germinal material
has changed only in that it has become simpler.

Natural Selection

DARWIN

Of the four great historical speculations about
evolution, the doctrine of Natural Selection of Darwin and Wallace has met with the most widespread
acceptance. Later the theory will be examined more
critically. Here only its broadest aspects will be
considered.

Darwin appealed to *chance variations* as supply-
ing evolution with the material on which natural selection works. If we accept, for the moment, this
statement as the cardinal doctrine of natural selection it may appear that evolution is due, (1) *not* to
an *orderly* response of the organism to its environment, (2) *not* in the main to the adjustment of the
animal through the use or disuse of its parts, (3)
not to any innate non-physical principle of living
material itself, and (4) above all *not* to purpose
either from within or from without. Darwin made
quite clear what he meant by chance. By chance he
did not mean that the variations were not causal.
On the contrary he taught that in science we mean
by chance only that the particular combination of
causes that bring about a variation is not known.

They are accidents, it is true, but they are causal accidents.

In his famous book on *Animals and Plants under Domestication,* Darwin dwells at great length on the nature of the conditions that bring about variations. If some of his views seem to us today at times vague, at times problematical, and often without a secure basis, nevertheless we find, in every instance, that Darwin was searching for the *physical causes of variation.* He brought, in consequence, conviction to many minds that there are abundant indications, even if certain proof is lacking, that the causes of variation are to be found in natural processes.

Today the belief that evolution takes place by means of natural processes is generally accepted. It did not seem probable that we should ever again have to renew the old contest between evolution and special creation.

But this is not enough. We can never remain satisfied with a negative conclusion of this kind. We must find out what natural causes bring about variations in animals and plants; and we must also find out what kinds of variations are inherited, and how they are inherited. If the circumstantial evidence for organic evolution, furnished by comparative anatomy, embryology and paleontology is cogent, we should expect to observe evolution going on at the present time, i.e., we should be able to observe the occurrence of variations and their transmission. This has actually been done by the geneticist. Certain kinds of new characters have been seen to arise by a process called mutation and their inheritance is now known to follow Mendel's laws.

CHAPTER III

THE EVIDENCE FOR ORGANIC EVOLUTION

FOUR branches of study have furnished the evidence of organic evolution: Comparative anatomy; Embryology; Paleontology; and Experimental Breeding or Genetics.

The Evidence from Comparative Anatomy

When we study animals and plants we find that they can be arranged in groups according to their resemblances. This is the basis of comparative anatomy, which is only an accurate study of facts that are superficially obvious to everyone.

The groups are based not on a single difference, but on a very large number of resemblances. Let us take for example the group of vertebrates.

The hand and the arm of man are similar to the hand and arm of the ape (*fig.* 4). The legs of man, monkey, dog, sheep, and the horse are made up of similar bones (*fig.* 5). The same parts are found in the leg of the lizard, the frog, and, even though less certainly, in the fins of fishes. Comparsion does not end here. We find similarities in the skull and backbones of these same animals; in the brain; in the digestive system; in the heart and blood vessels; in the muscles.

Each of these systems is very complex, but the

same general arrangement is found in all. Anyone familiar with the evidence will, I think, probably reach the conclusion either that these animals have been created on some preconceived plan, or else that they have some other bond that unites them; for we

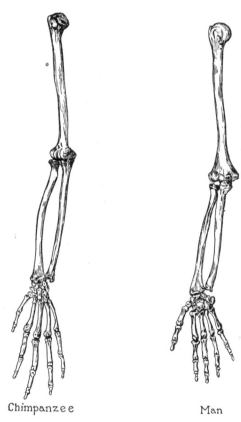

Chimpanzee   Man

FIG. 4.—Arm of chimpanzee and of man, drawn to scale. (*After Haeckel.*)

find it difficult to believe that such complex, yet similar, things could have arisen independently.

Because we can often arrange the series of structures in a line extending from the very simple to the

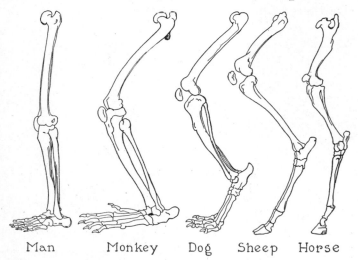

Man   Monkey   Dog   Sheep   Horse

Fig. 5.—Legs of five mammals, drawn to scale, to show homologous parts. (*After Leconte, from Romanes.*)

more complex, we are apt to become unduly impressed by this fact and conclude that if we found the complete series we should find all the intermediate steps and that they have arisen in the order of their complexity. For example, there have appeared in our cultures of the vinegar fly, Drosophila melanogaster (*fig.* 6) over four hundred new types that breed true. Each has arisen independently and suddenly. Every part of the body has been affected by one or another of these mutations. Many different kinds of changes have taken place in the wings and several of these involve the size of the wings. If we arrange the latter arbitrarily in the order of their size there will be an almost complete series begin-

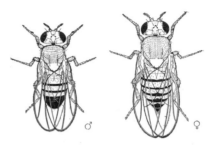

Fig. 6.—Male and female vinegar fly, Drosophila melanogaster.

ning with normal wings and ending with those of apterous flies. Several of these types are represented in *figure* 7. The order in which these mutations occurred bears no relation to their size; each originated independently from the wild type.

Mutations have occurred involving the pigmentation of the body and wings. The head and thorax of the wild Drosophila melanogaster are grayish yellow, the abdomen is banded with yellow and black, and the wings are gray. There have appeared in our cultures several kinds of darker types ranging to almost black flies and to lighter types that are pale yellow. If put in line a series may be made from the darkest flies at one end to the light yellow flies at the other. These types, with the fluctuations that occur within each type, furnish a complete series of gradations; yet historically they have arisen independently of each other.

Many changes in eye color have appeared. As

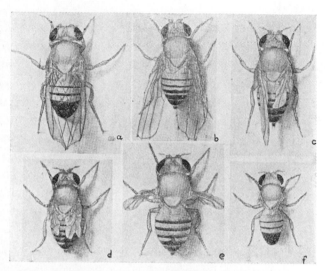

Fig. 7.—Mutants of Drosophila melanogaster, arranged in order of size of wings; *a*, cut,; *b*, beaded; *c*, stumpy; *d*, another stumpy; *e*, vestigial; *f*, apterous.

many as fifty or more races differing in eye color are now maintained in our cultures. Some of them are so similar that they can scarcely be separated from each other. It is easily possible beginning with the darkest eye color, sepia, which is deep brown, to pick out a perfectly graded series ending with pure white eyes. But such a serial arrangement would give a totally false idea of the way the different types have arisen; and any conclusion based on the existence of such a series might very well be entirely erroneous, for the fact that such a series exists bears no relation to the order in which its members have appeared.

Suppose that evolution "in the open" had taken place in the same way, by means of *discontinuous* variation. What value then would the evidence from comparative anatomy have in so far as it is based on a continuous series of variants of any organ?

No one familiar with the entire evidence will doubt for a moment that these four hundred races of Drosophila belong to the same species and have had a common origin, for while they may differ mainly in one thing they are extremely alike in a hundred other things, and in the general relation of the parts to each other.

It is in this sense that the evidence from comparative anatomy can be used, I think, as an argument for evolution. It is the resemblances that the animals or plants in any group have in common that is the basis for such a conclusion; it is not because we can arrange any particular variations in a continuous series. In other words, our inference concerning the common descent of two or more species is based on the totality of such resemblances that still remain in large part after each change has taken place. In this sense the argument from comparative anatomy, while not a demonstration, furnishes circumstantial evidence too strong to be disregarded.

The Evidence from Embryology

In passing from the egg to the adult the individual goes through a series of changes. In the course of this development we see not only the beginnings of the organs that gradually enlarge and change into those of the adult animal, but also see some organs appear and later disappear before the adult stage is reached. We find, moreover, that the young sometimes resemble in a most striking way the adult stage of groups that we place lower in the scale of evolution.

Many years before Darwin advanced his theory of evolution through natural selection, the resemblance of the young of higher animals to the adults of lower animals had attracted the attention of zoologists and various views, often very naïve, had been advanced to account for the resemblance. Among these speculations there was one practically identical with that adopted by Darwin and the post-Darwinians, namely that the higher animals repeat in their development the *adult stages* of lower animals. Later this view became one of the cornerstones of the theory of organic evolution. It reached its climax in the writings of Haeckel, and I think I may add without exaggeration that for twenty-five years it furnished the chief inspiration of the school of descriptive embryology. Today it is taught in many textbooks of biology. Haeckel called this interpretation the Biogenetic Law. The parallel between the historical development of antlers of deer (*fig.* 8) and their postnatal development from year to year (*fig.* 9) is most striking. Historically we may suppose that the development was due to the appear-

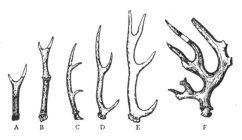

Fig. 8.—Fossil deer antlers. The first two to the left are from the mid-eosine; the third is from the upper miocene; the fourth is from the pliocene, as is also the fifth figure. The figure to the right is from the "forest-bed of Norfolk." (*After Romanes.*)

ance of hereditary variations in the germ material. At the present time, the stages in their development are closely correlated with age, size, and especially with the yearly increase in the internal secretion of the testes; for, after castration the antlers no longer develop. In living deer all the hereditary factors that appeared in the past are present at each stage, but the extent to which the antlers develop depends on the physiological conditions mentioned above. In other words, while there is a close relation in both cases

between the hereditary factors present, the causes
that led to the development of the more complicated
stages in the past (the accumulation of hereditary
factors) are different from the causes that, at pres-

FIG. 9.—Antlers of stag,
showing successive additions
of branches in successive
years. (*After Romanes.*)

ent, bring about a similar sequence as the individual
gets older.

It was early recognized that many embryonic
stages could not possibly represent ancestral animals.
A young fish with a huge yolk sac attached (*fig.* 10)
could scarcely ever have led a free life as an adult
individual. Such stages were interpreted, however,
as *embryonic* additions to the original ancestral

6851

type. The embryo had done something on its own account.

In some animals the young have structures that attach them to the mother, as does the placenta of the

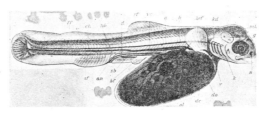

Fig. 10.—Young trout, six days after hatching. (*After Ziegler.*)

mammals. In other cases the young develop membranes about themselves—like the amnion of the chick (*fig.* 11) and mammal—that would have shut off an adult animal from all intercourse with the out-

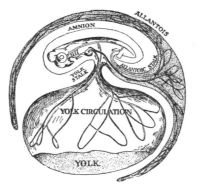

Fig. 11.—Diagram of chick, showing relations of amnion, allantois, and yolk. (*After Wilder.*)

side world. Hundreds of such embryonic structures are known. These were explained as embryonic adaptations and hence falsifications of the ancestral records.

At the end of the last century Weismann injected a new idea into our views concerning the origin of variations. He urged that variations are germinal, i.e., they first appear in the egg and the sperm as changes that later bring about modifications in the individual. The idea has been fruitful and is generally accepted by most biologists today. It means that the offspring of a pair of animals are not affected by the structure or the activities of their parents, but the germ material is the unmodified stream from which both the parent and the young have arisen. Hence their resemblance. Now, it has been found that a variation arising in the germ material, no matter what its cause, may affect any stage in the development of the next individuals that arise from it. There is no reason to suppose that such a change produces a new character that always sticks itself, as it were, on to the end of the old series. This idea of germinal variation therefore carried with it the death of the older conception of evolution by superposition.

In more recent times another idea has become current, mainly due to the work of Bateson and of de Vries—the idea that variations are discontinuous. Such a conception does not fall easily into line

with the statement of the biogenetic "law"; for
actual experience with discontinuous variation has
taught us that new characters that arise do not add
themselves to the end of the line of already existing
characters but if they involve adult characters they
change them without, as it were, passing through
and beyond them.

I venture to think that these new ideas and this
new evidence have played havoc with the biogenetic
"law." Nevertheless, there is an interpretation of
the facts that is entirely compatible with the theory
of evolution. Let me illustrate this by an example.

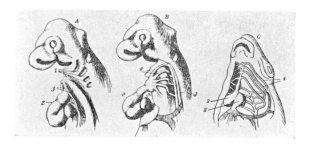

Fig. 12.—Diagram of head of chick, *A* and *B*, showing
gill slits and aortic arches; and head of fish, *C*, showing
aortic arches. (*After Hesse.*)

The embryos of the chick (*fig.* 12) and of man
(*fig.* 13) possess at an early stage in their development
gill slits on the sides of the neck like those of fishes.
No one familiar with the relations of the parts will

for a moment doubt that the gill slits of these embryos and of the fish represent the same structures.
When we look further into the matter we find that

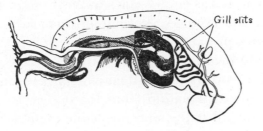

FIG. 13.—Human embryo, showing gill slits
and aortic arches. (*After His, from Marshall.*)

young fish also possess gill slits (*fig.* 14)—even in
young stages in their development. Is it not then
more probable that the mammal and bird possess

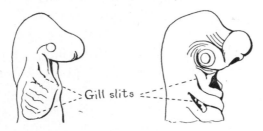

FIG. 14.—Side views of head of embryo shark,
showing gill slits. (*After Sedgwick.*)

this stage in their development simply because it
has never been lost? Is not this a more reasonable
view than to suppose that the gill slits of the embryos of the higher forms represent the adult gill

slits of the fish that in some mysterious way have been pushed back into the embryo of the bird?

Many similar examples could be given. All can be interpreted as embryonic survivals rather than as phyletic contractions. Not one of them calls for the latter interpretation.

The study of the cleavage pattern of the segmenting egg furnishes the most convincing evidence that a different explanation from the one stated in the biogenetic law is the more probable explanation.

It has been found that the cleavage pattern has the same general arrangement in the early stages of flat worms, annelids and molluscs (*fig.* 15). Obviously these stages have never been adult ancestors, and obviously if their resemblance has any historical meaning at all, it is that each group has retained the same general plan of cleavage, possessed by their common ancestor.

Accepting this view, does the evidence from embryology favor the theory of evolution? I think that it does very strongly. The embryos of the mammal, bird, and lizard have gill slits today because gill slits were present in the embryos of their common ancestors. There is no other view that explains so well their presence in the higher forms.

It may be asked whether this is not all that the "biogenetic law"claims. Has not the old conclusion been reached in a roundabout way? I think not. To my mind there is a wide difference between the old

statement that the higher animals living today have
the original adult stages telescoped into their embryos, and the statement that the resemblance be-

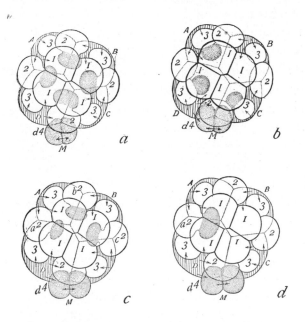

Fig. 15.—Cleavage stages of four types of eggs; *a*,
Planarian; *b*, Annelid; *c*, Mollusc (Crepidula); *d*,
Mollusc (Unio).

tween certain characters in the embryos of higher
animals and corresponding stages in the embryos of
lower animals is most plausibly explained by the assumption that they have descended from the same
ancestors, and that their common structures are embryonic survivals.

The Evidence from Paleontology

The direct evidence furnished by fossil remains
is by all odds the strongest evidence that we have in
favor of organic evolution. Paleontology holds the
incomparable position of being able to point directly
to fossil remains showing that the animals and
plants living in past times are connected with those
living at the present time, often through an unbroken series of stages (*fig.* 16). Paleontology has
triumphed over the weakness of the evidence, which
Darwin admitted was serious, by filling in many of
the missing links.

Paleontology has been criticised on the ground
that it cannot pretend to show the actual ancestors
of living forms, because, if in the past genera and
species were as abundant and as diverse as we find
them at present, it is very improbable that the bones
of any individual that happened to be preserved are
the bones of just that species that took part in the
evolution. Paleontologists freely admit that in many
cases this is probably true, but even then the evidence is still, I think, just as valuable and in exactly
the same sense as is the evidence from comparative
anatomy. It suffices that there lived in the past a
particular "group" of animals that had many points
in common with those that preceded them and with
those that came later. Whether these are the actual
ancestors, or not, does not so much matter; for, the
view that, from such a group of species, the later

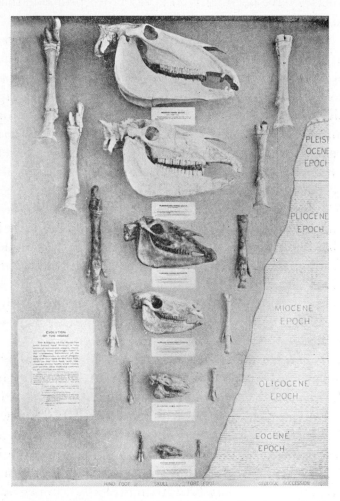

FIG. 16.—Evolution of the horse, showing the changes in the skull and in the bones of the legs. (*After Matthews.*)

species have been derived is far more probable than any other view that has been proposed.

With this unrivalled material and splendid series of gradations, paleontology has constructed many stages in the past history of the globe. But paleontologists have sometimes gone beyond this descriptive phase of the subject and have attempted to formulate the "causes," "laws" and "principles" that have led to the development of their series. It has even been claimed that paleontologists are in a much better position than are zoologists to discover such principles, because they know both the beginning and the end of the evolutionary series. The reply is obvious. In his sweeping and poetic vision the paleontologist may fail completely to find out the nature of the pigments that have gone into the painting of his picture, and he may confuse a familiarity with the different views he has enjoyed of the canvas, with a knowledge of how the painting was done.

When the modern student of variation and heredity—the geneticist—looks over the different "continuous" series, from which certain "laws" and "principles" have been deduced, he is struck by two facts: that the gaps, in some cases, are enormous as compared with the single changes with which he is familiar, and (what is more important) that they involve numerous parts in many ways. Since the paleontologist does not know, and from the nature of the case cannot know whether the differences are due to one change or to a thousand he cannot with any certainty tell anything about the hereditary units which have made the process of evolution possible. Without this knowledge there can be no satisfactory understanding of the origin of new hereditary variations through which evolution is possible.

The Evidence from Genetics

In recent years a study of the origin of new characters has led to the discovery that sudden changes appear at times in the germinal elements— changes that have an effect on one or more characters of the organism. The process by which the change takes place is called mutation, and the new kind of individual it produces is called a mutant. The mutants breed true to the new type. How far, and in what sense, the occurrence of mutants suffices to supply the material for evolution in animals and plants is one of the important biological problems of today.

While in a strict sense genetics deals only with the mode of transmission of the hereditary elements (the genes) from parent to offspring, the scientific study of the origin of new variations is undertaken today almost exclusively by students of genetics, and is now recognized as a part of their work. I shall include, therefore, under the "evidence from genetics" the origin of new characters by mutation.

In many groups of animals and plants new kinds

of individuals have been seen to suddenly appear. The new characters that they show are transmitted to their descendants. In some cases the new characters depart widely from those of the stock from which the new individual has sprung; in other cases the departure may be very slight and pass unnoticed unless one is very familiar with the parent stock. In fact, it is owing, in large part, to a minute examination of plants and animals, that many of the new characters studied by geneticists have been discovered. So small are some of the observed changes that they are not greater than the fluctuating changes due to the environment. The inheritance of the new character, when it is as slight as this, can only be determined by a careful study of successive generations under controlled conditions both genetic and environmental. It is the realization of these requirements that has enabled genetics to make its contribution to the theory of evolution.

While it is true that most of these mutant changes have been observed in animals under domestication, or in species that have recently been brought into the laboratory, there is no evidence that they owe their appearance to cultivation or to domestication. On the contrary similar mutants have been found in wild species. Cultivated plants and domesticated animals are more familiar to us, and more carefully scrutinized, than are wild species. Hence in large part the more frequent discovery of new types in these forms.

Many, probably most, of the extreme mutant types could not compete with the native types from which they have sprung, and this has been urged as an argument against the view that mutants could furnish the materials for evolution; because, it is said, only better adapted types could survive that have an advantage of some sort over the parent types so that they can replace the original types, or else find a new environment to which they are better suited than were the original forms. This argument, if it could be substantiated, would be a fatal blow to the mutation theory of evolution. It calls, therefore, for careful and impartial consideration. That it is not justified is shown, I think, by the following evidence.

While it is true that many of the mutant characters that are preserved by geneticists for a study of heredity are extreme departures from the original type, these are utilized rather than smaller differences because they are easily observed and their classification readily determined. Those characters that depart little from the parent type, or are difficult to distinguish from the fluctuating variations of that type, are more difficult to study and are neglected. Hence has arisen in some quarters the erroneous idea that all mutant types are defectives and incapable of competing with the original form.

In this connection it is important to keep in mind the fact that animals and plants are extremely complex machines that are highly adapted to the conditions of life in which they live. Any change, and especially any great change in them, is far more likely to throw them out of balance with their environment than to bring to them an advantage, but it is possible, nevertheless, that some of the changes, however slight, might be beneficial, especially those that add to or diminish slightly some important character or function already present. These changes might furnish materials for evolution.

Darwin rested his case for evolution on the observed small differences that all animals and plants show. Now, while we realize today that many of these slight differences are not inherited, we also know that amongst them there are some that are inherited, and that these, so far as we know, have arisen as mutations. At present there is no evidence that will stand the test of criticism in favor of any other origin than that all known variations owe their appearance to the same process of mutation that also produces the larger differences; and, I repeat, that there is much explicit evidence to show that very small differences, that add to or subtract from characters already present, do appear by mutation.

Finally there is evidence that the differences shown by individuals in nature are inherited in the same way as are the observed mutant characters of domesticated forms. While this identity in the method of inheritance may not be a conclusive argument in itself in showing that in both cases the differences have arisen by the same process, still the probability is so strong that it would be short-sighted to reject it, when the alternative assertion that the differences in the wild form have had a different origin, has nothing to support it. These questions will come up again for further consideration, but enough has been said to show that the discovery of the way in which new characters appear and are inherited marks a distinct advance in our study of the evolutionary process.

CHAPTER IV

THE MATERIALS OF EVOLUTION

THE apparent permanence of the types of animals and plants living at the present time is a common fact of observation. If this were the whole story it would appear that evolution had come to an end. If living things at the present time were really stable, we could give no good reason why it has not always been so in the past. On the other hand, if this stability is deceptive, we might expect to find evolution still taking place at the present time as in the past, and if this is true we might hope by a careful study of what is happening in living things about us to be able to get some information as to the way in which the process has taken place in the past. It is, of course, also conceivable that, even if evolution went on in the past, it has actually come to an end at the present time, or at least, having reached its climax, a declining process may be the order of the day—a process the reverse of that by which the upward trend of evolution went on in the past. It is also conceivable that the process of evolution is so slow that we may not be able to detect or measure it with means at our disposal. It may be true, furthermore, that certain species at least have become so far adjusted to the present conditions of the earth, that they are no longer advancing, and that only a few species are producing new or better types.

While it is well to keep these possibilities in mind, an appeal to the actual evidence furnishes no grounds for the belief that the process of evolution has come to an end. The conditions of land, water, and atmosphere have in all probability changed slowly since life first appeared, as they are changing today, and if in the past, evolution has progressed while the external world has been so slowly changing, it is a fair presumption that, to some extent at least, we may expect to find evolution taking place at the present time. It should also not be forgotten that the readjustment of animals and plants to each other may be as important a condition of evolution as their adjustments to the external world. From the latter point of view, the extraordinary complexity of the relation of living things to each other may even seem to furnish ample opportunities for further adjustments. It is certain, at least, that with the advent of man's interference with the natural conditions essential to other animals and plants, widespread changes may be expected to take place in part destructive but possibly also constructive. His domestication of several kinds of plants has produced changes in them that are very striking, but whether by the same kind of processes that take place in nature is a matter of dispute.

There is then, on the whole, a fair *a priori* expectation that evolution may still be taking place, and that it may not be so slow as to be beyond our powers of observation and even experimentation. The study of living things has, I think, confirmed this expectation despite the fact that there exist at present rather wide differences of opinion as to the legitimate conclusions from the evidence.

A great deal of the discussion about evolution has centered about the *Origin of Species*. Historically, the question as to what constitutes a species goes back at least as far as Linné (1707-1778) who classified all plants and animals known to him into such groups. The systematic arrangement of living things into species, genera, families, etc., still attracts the attention of a large number of naturalists.

Many difficulties arise when an attempt is made to arrange animals into groups. It is generally recognized that, in some groups, species have a different value from that in others. While some taxonomists prefer to arrange individuals into large species, other systematists split these large species into several or many smaller ones, still calling them species. It is generally admitted that the classification into species is often an arbitrary procedure, one that is useful, of course, in order to indicate the resemblances and differences that a study of animals and plants reveals. A few students of the subject still attempt to arrange their species in such a way as to indicate their relationship by descent, but the attempt, while desirable from the standpoint of evolution, has proven so difficult that it has been tacitly abandoned or ignored by many taxonomists.

It is unfortunate, in my opinion, that ever since the time of Darwin the question of the origin of species has occupied so much of the forefront of speculation concerning the evolution of living things; for if, as I have stated, "species" are to a large extent arbitrary arrangements of animals and plants—arrangements that may be essential for the purpose for which they are made, but entirely unsuited for evolutionary study—many unnecessary difficulties may arise in an attempt to explain their origin by natural processes, if some species are only groups of individuals arranged by taxonomists for convenience.

Nevertheless, there are certain important considerations connected with attempts to classify living things into species that cannot be dismissed by the foregoing treatment of the subject.

In the first place, experience has shown that most animals and plants do fall into groups that are more like each other than like other groups; and in the second place, that within each group the individuals freely cross and leave fertile offspring, while between most species crossing is rare or impossible, and when it occurs the offspring are generally sterile. When two types are infertile with each other they are generally admitted to be "good species" and even when they produce offspring, if the latter are sterile, the two types are recognized as separate species. It becomes necessary, therefore, to examine further into the significance of these relationships.

There are found in nature many interbreeding individuals that are sharply defined from other groups. It is convenient to have a name for all of the individuals of such a group, even when, as in the human species, the individuals living in the different parts of the world may present striking differences in structure, color, temperament, and social behavior. There are other types that are different from all others within a circumscribed region, but in other regions are represented by individuals that show slight but constant differences from the former. Here it becomes a more difficult matter to decide whether to call them all one species or whether to make two species. In practice it is generally agreed amongst taxonomists to give one specific name to such groups, if intermediate forms between the groups are found, but, if intermediate types are absent, the two separated groups are called different species. It is obvious, therefore, that the distinction between such species is largely arbitrary and artificial, especially since in the great majority of cases no tests of cross-breeding are made to determine whether the extreme types will cross and leave fertile offspring, or whether they are infertile or if fertile leave sterile offspring.

That the visible structural differences between groups of individuals is not a safe guide on which to construct a real distinction, is exemplified by numerous cases in which groups may exist side by side, that are so closely similar that only an expert can separate them, yet are either infertile when crossed or else leave offspring that are sterile. For example, two species of Drosophila, often found together, are so similar that complete separation is extraordinarily difficult. They can be made to cross only after many matings, but the offspring are completely sterile. With this information at hand no one would hesitate to call them different species, while without it the two would be placed in the same species.

It is true, in general, that the more "different" in structure two groups are, the smaller the chance that they will be found to cross, and still smaller the chance that they will have fertile offspring. This brings us back to the second question concerning the relation of infertility between species and the sterility of species hybrids. The infertility may appear at first sight to be due to the observed differences, but there may be some other less obvious relation that is responsible for their failure to produce offspring. Darwin was familiar with this problem and has written about it extensively. He pointed out that there are no sharp lines with respect to infertility between species, and gave many examples, especially in plants, in which cross fertilization between individuals belonging to groups, unmistakably species according to ordinary standards, takes place. Darwin was also impressed by the fact that even self-sterility often occurs in hermaphroditic species, not only because self-fertilization is often made difficult in one way or another, but also because it does not actually occur even when the sperm has access to the egg, as has been shown by suitable tests.

Darwin was also familiar with the sterility of hybrids from species-crosses, and here again he emphasized the lack of any sharp distinction; for in some cases the sterility is complete, in others partial, and in still others it is not present. All this is in harmony with his conception of the gradual breaking up of a species into new groups or varieties which as they become more and more different may show, when crossed, various degrees of fertility, and of sterility in their offspring.

Since Darwin, the subject has not advanced much further, although genetics has contributed a little more information and holds out promise of furnishing more. It has been shown in one or two hermaphroditic species that genetic factors are present that are concerned with self-sterility, and in a few other cases it has been shown that similar conditions are explicable on the assumption of more than one such

factor. It has been found both in plants (tobacco)
and in one animal (Ciona) that the failure to self-
fertilize is not due to incompatibility of any sort between the egg and the sperm, but to a physiological
block to the penetration of the sperm into the egg. It
has also been shown in the case of several marine
animals (sea urchins and fishes) that the eggs may
be entered by spermatozoa of widely separated species—belonging even to different families—and
start development. The failure to produce a normal
embryo is due in some cases to the failure of the
sperm to develop normally in the foreign egg; in
other cases to the failure of the chromosomes derived
from the two sources to become normally distributed
in the cleavages of the egg, and in still other cases
to the inability of the introduced chromosomes to
function in the cytoplasm of the foreign egg.

All this is satisfactory and carries us a step further in an understanding of the problem of the infertility between species. We may add a further consideration in line with what genetics and embryology
lead us to expect, namely, that the genetic factors
present in the chromosomes of the fertilized egg
derived in part from the egg, in part from the sperm,
are acting on the cytoplasm throughout the process
of development. So long as these pairs of factors are
alike or identical (one maternally derived, one pater-
nally) the course of development runs smoothly,
but if one member of the pair acts in a different way

from the other member it is easy to see why sooner or later the result is disastrous owing to a conflict of competing factors.

The egg's cytoplasm that has been formed under the dual influence of the maternal set of chromosomes appears to determine the early stages of development so that even if the sperm introduces factors that would act disastrously on these stages their influence does not at first show itself, but as development proceeds the influence of the paternal chromosomes comes more and more into play and further progress is arrested. This is, in fact, what is seen, in a way, when widely different species of echinoderms or of fish are crossed. The early stages of cleavage run smoothly and follow the maternal type, but as the embryo develops further, irregularities and delays occur that bring progress to an end.

Thus while some advance has been made in the study of infertility between species, the other problem, namely the sterility of the hybrids, when such are produced between species not too different, is not so well understood, but in some cases at least the immediate cause of the sterility has been found. It has been shown, in recent years, to result from changes that take place in the ripening of the germ-cells. There comes a time when the pairs of chromosomes unite throughout their length and subsequently separate to go into sister cells. This is the so-called conjugation process. Now in certain hy-

brids, the mule for example, it has been shown that
the maternal and paternal chromosomes fail to pass
successfully through this ordeal with the result that
later they are separated very irregularly. In consequence the germ-cells contain all kinds of assort-
ments of the chromosomes and become abnormal.
The result is that the individual is sterile.

While these observations do not explain why the
chromosomes fail to unite, they do account for the
sterility of the hybrid. Until we learn more concerning the conditions that bring about the union of the
chromosomes, it may be unsafe to offer any explanation of the process; nevertheless, for the present
at least, it is not irrational to ascribe the failure to
the differences in the hereditary factors carried by
the chromosomes of the two species.

Now while all this will, I think, be conceded as
theoretically possible, the fact remains that in no
case has a mutant type been seen to arise that has
produced individuals that are fertile *inter se*, but
sterile with the parent species.[1] Bateson has recently
emphasized this point and has insisted that until it
can be met we are not justified in assuming that new
species are formed by mutation.

He says: "The production of an indubitably sterile hybrid from completely fertile parents which
have arisen under critical observation from a com-

[1] Plough has recently reported a case that comes very near to fulfilling
these conditions.

mon origin,"—this "is the event for which we wait."

Bateson has worded his requirements in such a way as to render the demonstration well-nigh impossible, but a somewhat different view, of the origin of species through mutation may put the problem in another form where theoretically at least the difficulty is lightened even if not entirely removed.

Suppose on Bateson's supposition that a germ-cell has been produced in a male or in a female that contains a single mutant gene having the required property of forming a sterile hybrid. In order to perpetuate itself, this germ-cell would have to meet a normal germ-cell. The single individual that resulted would by the very conditions imposed be itself sterile; for, since there are no other individuals of the kind in existence there would be no means of finding out that the single individual would have been fertile with one of its kind. It would, therefore, be lost because of its sterility.

The possibilities are not much better even if we assume that the mutation occurred early in the germ-track, so that several or many germ-cells came to contain the mutant gene. When crossed back to the parent stock several sterile individuals would appear, which brings the experiment to a disastrous end as before. If on the other hand two such individuals should by chance mate then a new race might be started which tested to the original race would be found to produce offspring that are sterile. Here the conditions are fulfilled, but the chance of recording such a result at the time would be small indeed unless the sterile gene itself carried with it some other landmark, some new character, that would direct attention to it from the beginning. Something of the sort appears, in fact, to have happened in a stock of Drosophila studied by Plough where a new race appeared whose individuals are more fertile *inter se* than with the parent stock.

The conditions for producing a hybrid sterile race may appear more favorable in a monoecious form, as in a plant with stamens and pistils in the same flower. While a mutation in a single germ-cell would again not improve the situation, yet if mutation occurred early in the germ-track, and both pollen grains and ovules came to contain the gene, self-fertilization would start a race that fulfils the requirements. These if inbred would then be found to be fertile *inter se* and produce fertile offspring, and with the parent type they would produce sterile hybrids.

It is obvious, as I have said, that the chance of detecting such a mutant type would be very small unless its mutation involved some other character than the one under discussion so that it could be at once recorded.

The necessity of putting the Mutation Theory to the test that Bateson calls for, seems to me very doubtful, for while this is one of the possible ways in which a mutant type might split off at once from the parent type it is by no means the only way, or even, I think, the most probable way in which species have become separated.

I venture also to question the importance ascribed to the sterility of the hybrid as a criterion of the origin of species. The test is arbitrary and not called for by the evidence at hand relating to sterile hybrids between species. There are no such sharp distinctions, as implied in the test, between groups found in nature that are called species.

The interpretation of the infertility between species and the sterility of hybrids that seems to me more probable is very different from that suggested by Bateson. Both phenomena, as I interpret them, are the result of many kinds of differences that have arisen in two species that have been separated for a long time. Each has taken on new characters due to mutational changes of different sorts. There is no one problem of infertility of species and no one problem of the sterility of hybrids, but many problems, each due to differences that have arisen in the germinal material. One or more of these differences may affect the mechanism of fertilization or the process of development, producing some incompatibility.

In order that a species may split up into one or more new species in the way suggested, isolation is implied. Isolation may be due to difference in local-

ity, but it may also come about by individuals within
the same area ripening their germ cells at different
times, etc.

If species arise in this way we avoid the difficulty
raised by Bateson concerning the origin of sterility
of hybrids whose parents have arisen through mutation. Moreover the difficulty is not one peculiar to
the mutation theory, but applies in large part to any
theory that postulates the origin of one species from
another.

If then we dismiss the problems that have grown
out of the historical definitions of species, and turn
directly to an examination of the origin of new variations we shall find that some progress has been
made since Darwin wrote, and that this new knowledge supports Darwin's view that the variations
shown by animals and plants furnish materials for
a theory of evolution. There is evidence that new
characters suddenly arise by mutation both in domesticated and in wild types, and that these variations are inherited in the same way as are the differences present in wild types that distinguish them
from one another. In addition there are variations
(fluctuations) due to the action of the environment
on the developing individual. These are not inherited
and cannot therefore take part in evolution. These
statements will be discussed in later chapters after
Mendel's laws, and some other laws of heredity discovered since his time, have been examined.

CHAPTER V
MENDEL'S TWO LAWS OF HEREDITY

GREGOR MENDEL studied the heredity of certain characters of the common edible pea, in the garden of the monastery at Brünn. In the account of his work published in 1865, he said:

It requires indeed some courage to undertake a labor of such a far-reaching extent; it appears, however, to be the only right way by which we can finally reach the solution of a question the importance of which cannot be over-estimated in connection with the history of the evolution of organic forms.

He tells us also why he selected peas for his work:

The selection of the plant group which shall serve for experiments of this kind must be made with all possible care if it be desired to avoid from the outset every risk of questionable results.

The experimental plants must necessarily

1. Possess constant differentiating characters.
2. The hybrids of such plants must, during the flowering period, be protected from the influence of all foreign pollen, or be easily capable of such protection.

Mendel succeeded not only because of his foresight in planning the experiments, and in keeping

an exact record of the numbers of individuals of
different kinds that appeared in the second and third
generations, but also because of his insight in interpreting the results that he obtained.

Others had made crosses before Mendel. In fact,
a great deal of work had been done in making crosses
between wild species and also between cultivated
varieties. We realize today that the earlier crosses
between species failed to reveal the laws of heredity
because so many characters were involved that the
relationship of contrasted characters was obscured,
and that the crosses between domesticated varieties
failed either because the materials were not well
chosen, or else because the numerical relations in
the second generation were not observed. Some of
the earlier hybridologists, who worked before Mendel's time and at about the same period, had observed that the parental types may reappear in the
second and later generations. Naudin (1863, 1868)
had even suggested that this reappearance is due to
the separation of the parental types in the hybrid
but he failed to detect the numerical relations involved and he did not make out the independent
inheritance of the members of different pairs of
characters.

About twenty years after Mendel's results were
first announced, but before his results became generally known, Galton (1889-) formulated several
laws of inheritance based in part on data from plants

and animals, and also from man. He studied the
problem from a statistical standpoint, as Mendel
had done, but in the material that Galton used, the
effects due to the environment were not separable
from those due to inherited factors. Moreover he
did not give sufficient weight to the fact that the
character of an individual is not a suitable index of
its hereditary constitution.

The latter difficulty was present in Mendel's
material also, and one of his chief merits is that he
detected this fact by making tests which revealed
the hereditary constitution of each individual.

Mendel deduced two laws of heredity that may be
called the Law of Segregation and the Law of Free
Assortment.

Mendel's First Law

Mendel's first law can be more strikingly illustrated today by examples other than those he gave.
The inheritance of the red and white colors of the
flowers of the common garden plant Mirabilis jalapa or four o'clock furnishes an excellent example.
If the pollen from a plant with white flowers is
placed on the pistil of a plant with red flowers, the
seeds that are produced give rise to a plant with
pink flowers (*fig.* 17). The hybrid may be said to
be intermediate in the color of its flowers between
the two parents. If the hybrid is self-fertilized it
produces white-, pink-, and red-flowered plants in

the proportion of $1:2:1$. All of these had the same ancestry, yet they are of three different kinds. If we did not know their history it would be quite impossible to state what the ancestry of the white or of

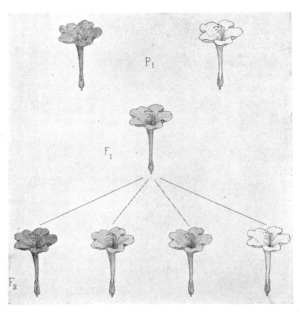

FIG. 17.—Inheritance of color in the four o'clock (Mirabilis jalapa). The figure above and to the left stands for a red flower, that above and to the right for a white flower. The next two generations are shown below.

the red had been, for they might just as well have come from pure white and pure red ancestors respectively as to have emerged from the pink hybrids. Moreover, when we test them we find that they are as pure as are white- or red-flowering plants that have had all white- or all red-flowering ancestors.

Mendel's Law explains the results of this cross as follows:

The egg-cell from the white parent carries a factor for white, the pollen-cell from the red parent carries a factor for red. The hybrid formed by their union carries both factors. The results of their combined action is to produce flowers intermediate in color.

When the hybrids mature and their germ-cells (eggs or pollen) ripen, each carries only one of these factors, either the red or the white (*fig.* 18), but not both. In other words, the two factors that have been brought together in the hybrid separate in its germ-

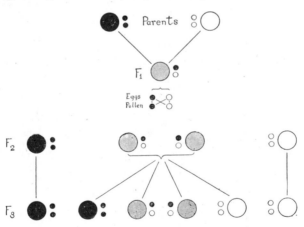

Fig. 18.—Diagram illustrating the transmission of the factors for red color (here black) and for white (here the open circles) in a cross between red and white flowered four o'clocks.

cells. Half of the egg-cells are white-bearing, half red-bearing. Half of the pollen-cells are white-bearing, half red-bearing. Chance combinations at fertilization give the three classes of individuals of the second generation.

The white-flowering plants should forever breed true, as in fact they do. The red-flowering plants also breed true. The pink-flowering plants, having the same composition as the hybrids of the first generation, should give the same kind of result. They give, in fact, this result, i.e., one white-, to two pink-, to one red-flowered offspring (*fig.* 18).

Another case of the same kind is known to breeders of poultry. One of the domesticated breeds is known as the Andalusian. It is a slate-blue bird shading into blue-black on the neck and back. Poultry men have known for a long time that these blue birds do not breed true but produce white, black, and blue offspring. The explanation of the failure to produce a pure race of Andalusians is that they are like the pink flowers of the four o'clock, i.e., they are a hybrid type formed by the meeting of the white and the black germ-cells. If the whites produced by the Andalusians are bred to the blacks, all the offspring will be blue (*fig.* 19).

When two such blue colored hybrid birds are bred to each other, chance fertilization of any egg by any sperm (*fig.* 20) will give one pure white, to two hybrid blues, to one pure black.

FIG. 19.—Cross between splashed white and black fowls, giving in F_1 blue Andalusian. In F_2 there is one splashed white, to two blues, to one black.

In the two cases just given the character of the hybrid is intermediate between the two contrasted characters of the parents; but in the seven pairs of contrasted characters studied by Mendel the character of the hybrid is like that of one of the parents. This character is said to be dominant. Two of Mendel's cases will serve to illustrate this relation. If a tall pea is crossed to a short pea the offspring are tall (*fig.* 21), i.e., not intermediate in height. If

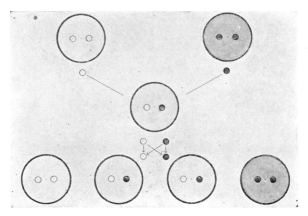

Fɪɢ. 20.—Diagram to show the distribution of the genes for white and for black in the Andalusian cross. (See *fig.* 19.)

these hybrids self-fertilize (or are bred to each other) there are two kinds of offspring, tall and short, produced in the ratio of three to one. The short peas, if self-fertilized, breed true (*fig.* 22), but if the tall peas are self-fertilized they are found to be of two kinds—one-third of them breed true and two-thirds of them produce three tall to one short offspring (*fig.* 22). It is obvious that here, as in the four o'clock and in the Andalusian fowl, there are present in the second generation three kinds of offspring in the proportion of one pure tall, to two hybrid talls, to one pure short. It is the discovery by Mendel of the existence of these three kinds of individuals in the second generation that enabled him to deduce his first law. He discovered that there

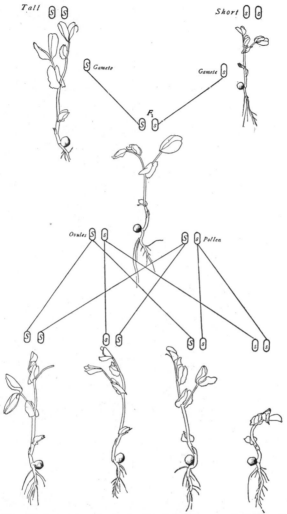

Fig. 21.—Diagram to illustrate the inheritance of tall and short, edible peas. The small letter, *s*, stands for the short-producing gene. The large letter, *S*, for its normal allelomorph or tall. Only the first and second generations are here shown. The second and third generations are shown in *fig. 22*.

were three such kinds of second generation individuals by following them into the next (third) generation. Had he been fortunate enough to have
worked with a form like the four o'clock where the
1:2:1 ratio is apparent in the second generation
this relation would probably have been seen without
carrying the experiment one generation further.

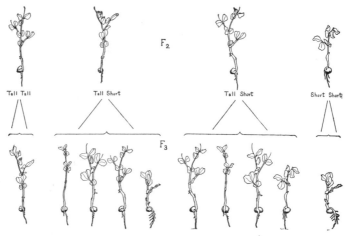

Fig. 22.—Diagram illustrating the results of self-pollination of the
F_2 plants of *fig. 21*. The results show that one of the tall F_2 plants is
pure for tall (tall-tall), that two of them are hybrid or heterozygous,
and that one is pure for short (short-short).

Mendel also crossed yellow and green peas (*fig.
23*). He crossed a plant belonging to a race having
yellow peas with one having green peas. The hybrid
plants had yellow seeds. These hybrids inbred gave
three yellows to one green seed. The explanation of
the results with peas is the same as that given for the

four o'clock. In the germ-cells of the hybrid—the so-called first fillial generation, or F_1—the elements (or factors) that come from the two parents separrate and half of the egg-cells come to carry one of

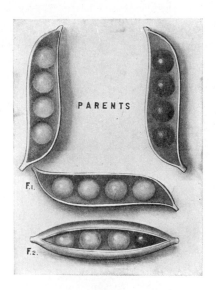

Fig. 23.—Diagram of cross between a yellow and a green pea.

the original elements and half the other element. Chance fertilization of any egg by any sperm (pollen) gives the numerical relation present in the next generation.

These four cases serve to illustrate an important fact. The character of the individual is not a measure of the nature of the mature germ-cells that it will produce. The pink F_1 hybrid four o'clock, that is intermediate, in a sense, between the white- and the red-flowered parents produces only white- and red-bearing germ-cells; and the yellow F_1 hybrid pea, whose color is exactly that of one of the parents, also produces two kinds of germ-cells in equal numbers, yellow- and green-producing. It is obvious from this that the character of the individual is not a reliable index of its ancestry, or of what it transmits to the next generation.

Mendel's Second Law

Besides his discovery that members of each pair of elements disjoin in the germ-cells of the hybrid (law of segregation) Mendel made a second discovery (the law of free assortment) which also has far-reaching consequences. The following case illustrates this second law.

If a pea that is yellow and round is crossed to one that is green and wrinkled (*fig.* 24), all of the offspring are yellow and round. Inbred, these give 9 yellow-round, 3 green-round, 3 yellow-wrinkled, 1 green-wrinkled. All the yellows taken together are to the green as 3:1. All the round taken together are to the wrinkled as 3:1; but some of the yellows are wrinkled and some of the green are round. There has been a recombination of characters, while at the same time the results, for each pair of characters taken separately, are in accord with Mendel's Law of Segregation. The second law of Mendel may be called the Law of Free Assortment of different character pairs. A character from one organism can, as it were, be transferred to a different organism.

The numerical results obtained, when two pairs

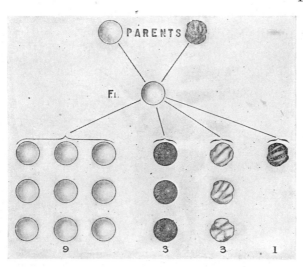

Fig. 24.—Diagram to show cross between a round-yellow and a green-wrinkled pea.

of characters are, as here, involved in the same cross, may be accounted for as follows. The element for green color may be represented by g and its contrasted color yellow by G, and the element for wrinkled by w and its contrasted character smooth by W. The egg of the yellow round parent pea is GW and the pollen of the green wrinkled pea is gw. The fertilized egg, that becomes the hybrid

(F_1), contains both sets of these elements; it is $GgWw$. These represented in pairs are:

$$\frac{G}{g} \quad \frac{W}{w}$$

Now when the germ-cells of this hybrid mature the members of one of the pairs behave independently of the members of the other pair. Consequently four kinds of germ-cells are possible, namely, GW, Gw, gW, gw (fig. 25). There will be four kinds of egg-

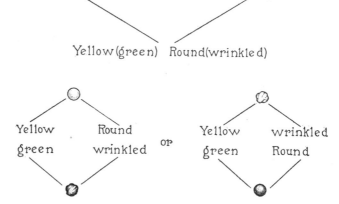

Fig. 25.—Diagram to show the independent segregation of the two pairs of factors, yellow-green and round-wrinkled.

cells in the hybrid and four kinds of pollen grains. Chance fertilization of any egg-cell by any pollen grain will give sixteen classes of individuals, as shown in figure 26.

There will be, as inspection of the table shows, 9

kinds of individuals that contain at least one G and one W; 3 kinds that will contain at least one G and two w's; 3 kinds that will contain at least one W and two g's; and one kind that will contain neither G nor

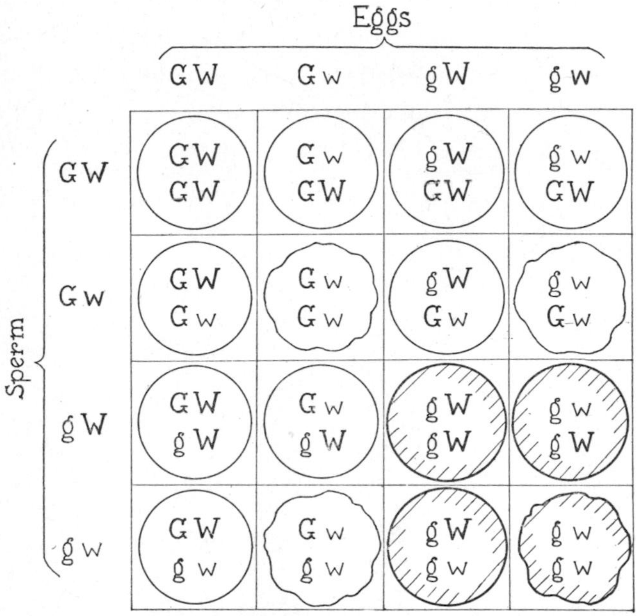

Fig. 26.—Diagram to show the sixteen combinations in F_2 when two pairs of factors are involved, namely, green, g, and yellow, G; wrinkled, w, and round, W.

W but two g's and two w's. Since yellow (G) dominates green (g), and round (W) dominates wrinkled (w) there will be

9 yellow-round:3 yellow-wrinkled:3 green-round:1 green-wrinkled.

vv EE   VV ee

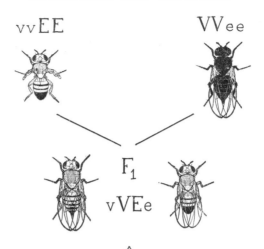

F₁
vVEe

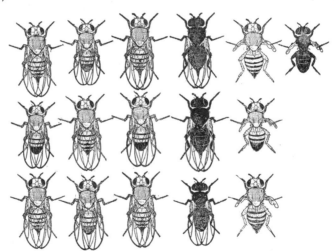

Fig. 27.—Diagram to show the independent inheritance of two pairs of factors, namely, gray (*EE*), vestigial (*vv*), and ebony (*ee*), long (*VV*). The lower group of 16 flies represents the 16 recombinations in the second, F_2, generation, in the ratio of 9:3::3:1.

Thus the independent assortment of the members of the two pairs of elements in the hybrid accounts for the kinds of individuals that appear in the next generation and also the proportion in which they occur.

Another illustration of Mendel's second law— one from the animal kingdom—is given in *figure* 27, for the vinegar fly. An ebony colored fly (e) with long wings (V) is crossed to a gray colored fly (E) with vestigial wings (v). The offspring (F_1) are gray flies with long wings, $EeVv$. If two of these hybrids (F_1's) are mated they produce 9 gray-long: 3 ebony-long: 3 gray-vestigial: 1 ebony-vestigial. The explanation (*fig.* 28) is the same as in the

Eggs	VE	Ve	vE	ve
Sperm				
VE	VE VE	Ve VE	vE VE	ve VE
Ve	VE Ve	Ve Ve	vE Ve	ve Ve
vE	VE vE	Ve vE	vE vE	ve vE
ve	VE ve	Ve ve	vE ve	ve ve

Fig. 28.—Diagram to show the composition of the 16 classes of individuals represented in F_2 of *fig.* 27.

peas when two pairs of contrasted characters are present.

The possibility of interchanging characters might be illustrated by hundreds of examples. It holds not only for two pairs of characters but when three, four, or more enter the cross. It is as though two individuals were taken apart and their characters were put together again by substituting one part for another.

Not only has this power to make whatever combinations we choose great practical importance, it has even greater theoretical significance; for it follows that the individual is not in itself the unit in heredity, but that within the germ-cells there exist smaller units concerned with the transmission of characters.

The older mystical statement of the individual as a unit in heredity has no longer any interest in the light of these discoveries, except as a past phase of biological history. We see, too, more clearly that the sorting out of factors in the germ plasm is a very different process from the influence of these factors on the development of the organism. There is today no excuse for confusing these two problems.

CHAPTER VI

THE CHROMOSOMES AND MENDEL'S TWO LAWS

THE discoveries that Mendel made with peas have been found to apply everywhere throughout the plant and animal kingdoms—to flowering plants, to mosses, to insects, snails, crustacea, fishes, amphibians, birds, and mammals (including man).

There must be something that these widely separated groups of plants and animals have in common—some simple mechanism perhaps—to give such definite and orderly series or results. There is, in fact, a mechanism, possessed alike by animals and plants, that fulfils the requirements of Mendel's principles.

The Cellular Basis of Heredity and Development

In order to appreciate the full force of the evidence, a few familiar facts, that became known before the discovery of the mechanism in question, may be briefly reviewed.

Throughout the greater part of the last century, while students of evolution and of heredity were engaged in what may be called the more general aspects of the subject, there existed another group of students who were engaged in working out the minute structure of the material basis of the living

organism. They found that organs such as the
brain, the heart, the liver, the lungs, the kidneys,
etc., are not themselves the units of structure, but
that all these organs can be reduced to a simpler
unit that repeats itself a thousand-fold in every organ. We call this unit a cell.

The egg is a cell, and the spermatozoon is a cell.
Fertilization is the union of two cells. Simple as the
process of fertilization appears to us today, its discovery swept aside a vast amount of mystical speculation concerning the rôle of the male and of the
female in the act of procreation.

Within the cell a new microcosm was revealed.
Every cell was found to contain a spherical body
called the nucleus (*fig.* 29). Within the nucleus is
a network of fibres; a sap fills the interstices of the

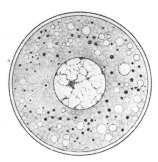

Fig. 29.—Diagram of a "typical cell,"
showing cell-wall, cytoplasm (with solid
and fluid inclusions) and centrosome
with astral rays (doubtfully present in
resting stage). In the center is the
nucleus with its network of chromatin,
and its nuclear sap.

network. The network resolves itself into a definite number of threads or rods at each division of the cell (*fig.* 30). These rods we call chromosomes. Each species of animals and plants possesses a characteristic number of chromosomes which have a definite size, and sometimes a specific shape, and even characteristic granules at different levels. Beyond this point our strongest microscopes fail to penetrate.

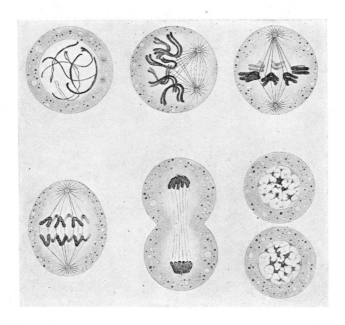

Fig. 30.—Diagram, slightly modified from Agar, to show a typical cell division (karyokinesis). The chromosomes are represented as black threads and rods, which pass onto the spindle fibres and then move to the poles of the spindle where they subsequently become vacuolated to form the resting nuclei of the two daughter cells.

Observation has reached, for the time being, its limit.

Certain evidence relating to inheritance through the sperm led to the conclusion that the chromosomes are the bearers of the hereditary units. If so, there should be many such units carried by *each* chromo-

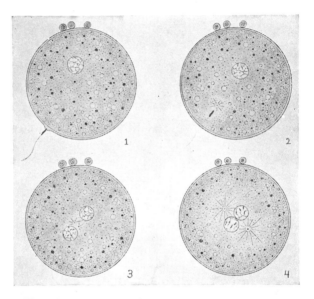

Fig. 31.—Diagram to show stages in fertilization of an egg by a spermatozoon. The three polar bodies lie at one pole, and the spermatozoon is represented as entering near the opposite side of the egg in 1 and 2. The head of the sperm swells up and moves towards the egg-nucleus, that has reformed after the polar bodies have been given off. A centrosome forms near the sperm-nucleus. It divides into two centrosomes, which begin to separate as a central spindle appears between them. Around each centrosome astral rays develop. The two nuclei come together in the middle of the egg to become the segmentation nucleus. A spindle develops around the nucleus.

some; for, the number of chromosomes is limited while the number of independently inherited characters is large. In Drosophila melanogaster it has been demonstrated not only that there are exactly

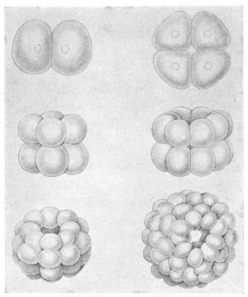

Fig. 32.—Diagram showing the segmentation of an egg into two, four, eight cells, etc. The cells become arranged over the surface of a sphere whose interior is filled with fluid. (*After Selenka.*)

as many groups of characters that are inherited together as there are pairs of chromosomes, but even that it is possible to locate the hereditary elements in particular chromosomes and to state the *relative position* there of the factors for the characters. If

the validity of this evidence is accepted, the study of
the cell leads to the ultimate units about which the
whole process of the transmission of the hereditary
factors turns.

Before considering this somewhat technical matter, certain facts, which are familiar for the most part,
should be recalled, because, on these, rests the whole
of the subsequent explanation.

The thousands of cells that make up the cell-state
that we call an animal or plant come from the fertilized egg (*fig.* 31). An hour or two after fertilization the egg divides into two cells (*fig.* 32). Then
each half divides again. Each quarter next divides.
The process continues until a large number of cells
is formed and, out of these, organs mold themselves.

At every division of the cell the chromosomes also
divide. Half of these have come from the mother,
half from the father. Every cell contains, therefore,
the sum total of all the chromosomes, and if these
are the bearers of the hereditary qualities, every cell
in the body, whatever its function, has a common
inheritance.

At an early stage in the development of the animal certain cells are set apart to form the organs of
reproduction. In some animals these cells can be
identified early in the cleavage (*fig.* 33).

The reproductive cells are at first like all the other
cells in the body in that they contain a full comple-
ment of chromosomes, half paternal and half mater-

nal in origin. They divide as do the other cells of the
body for a long time. At each division each chromosome splits lengthwise and its halves migrate to opposite poles of the spindle.

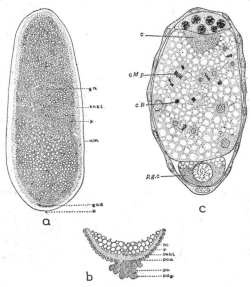

Fig. 33.—*a*, Section of egg of Calligrapha bigsbyana,
showing "germ-cell determinants" (granules), *g c d*,
at posterior end of egg; *b*, posterior end of a later
stage of same, showing primordial germ-cells; *c*, Section of egg of Miastor, showing single primordial
germ-cell at posterior end. (*After Hegner.*)

But there comes a time when a new process appears in the germ-cells (*figs.* 34 and 35). It is
essentially the same in the egg- and in the sperm-
cells. The discovery of this process we owe to the
laborious researches of many workers in many coun-

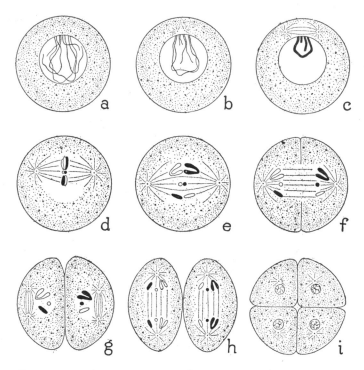

Fig. 34.—Diagram illustrating the two maturation divisions of the germ cells in the male. In *a* the chromosomes appear as thin threads (leptotene stage). These conjugate in pairs, *b*, beginning at the two ends of each loop. The threads contract, and a spindle appears, *d*, near the nucleus. The conjugating chromosomes enter the spindle, *d*. There they separate, *e*, moving to opposite poles of the spindle. The cell protoplasm begins to constrict, *f*. The chromosomes may without entering upon a resting nuclear stage pass onto a new spindle that has developed by the division of each of the centrosomes of each daughter cell, *g*. Each chromosome now splits throughout its length (equational division); half of each goes to one or the other pole. The two daughter cells then divide, giving four cells, each of which differentiates into a spermatozoon.

tries. The chromosomes come together in pairs (*fig.* 34). Each maternal chromosome conjugates with a paternal chromosome of the same kind.

Then follow two rapid divisions (*fig.* 34, *e-i*). At one of the divisions the double chromosomes separate (*fig.* 34, *d-f*) so that each resulting cell comes to contain some maternal and some paternal chromosomes, i.e., one or the other member of each pair. At the other division each chromosome simply splits as in ordinary cell division. In the male four spermatozoa

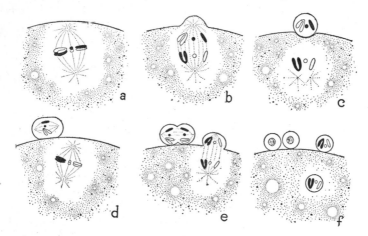

Fig. 35.—Diagram illustrating the two maturation divisions of the egg. In *a* the polar spindle is present at the periphery of the egg. The three pairs of chromosomes (bivalents) are represented in black and white; the white being the paternal and the black the maternal. In *b* the conjugating chromosomes have separated and are moving to the poles. In *c* the first polar body has been given off, leaving three single chromosomes in the egg. In *c* these have split lengthwise and lie off the equator of a new spindle. In *e* the daughter chromosomes have separated and moved to opposite poles. In *f* the second polar body has been given off and the first polar body has divided. Three single chromosomes are left in the egg.

are produced (by these two divisions) from each cell
of the testis (*fig*. 34, *i*).

In the female the two divisions of the egg-cell are
very unequal (*fig*. 35), although the chromosomes
are distributed equally to all the cells. Thus at the
first division one cell is very small (*fig*. 35, *c*) and is
called the polar body. At the next division the polar
body divides again, and at the same time the egg
divides again also, producing another polar body
(*fig*. 35, *d, e, f*). The three polar bodies and the egg-
cell are equivalent to the four spermatozoa, but only
the egg-cell undergoes further development—the
polar bodies disappear. Although only one cell sur-
vives, nevertheless there will be as many kinds of
mature eggs as there are kinds of sperm cells (with
respect to the distribution of the chromosomes), if,
as we now know to be the case, the distribution of
the chromosomes in the two final divisions (maturation divisions) are the same in the eggs and in the
sperm-cells. When the eggs are fertilized, each by
one spermatozoon, the whole number of chromosomes is restored.

The Mechanism of Mendel's Two Laws

The behavior of the chromosomes at the time of
maturation of the egg- and sperm-cells furnishes a
mechanism for Mendelian heredity if the chromosomes are the bearers of the hereditary elements, and
if they maintain their integrity both during the rest-

ing stages of the nucleus and during their period of active division. There is a great deal of evidence from direct observation in favor of this view and there is more evidence from the modern work in heredity that points in the same direction. This evidence can not be considered here, but if it is granted that these relations hold, then the behavior of the chromosomes during maturation furnishes, as stated above, an explanation of Mendel's laws.

An example will illustrate this statement. If in the four o'clock the elements for red flower color are carried in the red parent by the two members of the same pair of chromosomes and the elements for white flower color are carried in the white parent by two members of the same pair of chromosomes, the germ-cells (ripe egg- and sperm-cells) will each carry one of these chromosomes (*fig.* 36). If the red plant is crossed to the white, the pink hybrid will have a red- and a white-bearing chromosome.

When in the hybrid the germ-cells ripen, these two chromosomes, being mates, will come together as a pair and then separate at one of the two maturation divisions, and half of the eggs will contain the red-bearing chromosome and half will contain the white-bearing chromosome. Similarly for the pollen grains. Chance fertilization of any egg by any sperm will give the combinations of chromosomes that Mendel's law of segregation requires. In other words the known behavior of the chromosomes is exactly the same as Mendel's postulated elements.

Mendel's second law for the inheritance for two or more characters also finds its explanation in the behavior of the chromosomes, provided the members

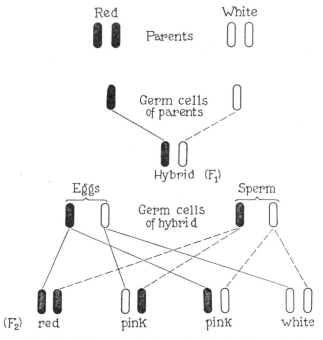

Red   White

Parents

Germ cells of parents

Hybrid (F₁)

Eggs   Sperm

Germ cells of hybrid

(F₂)   red   pink   pink   white

Fig. 36.—Diagram to illustrate the distribution of the chromosomes in a cross between a red and a white four o'clock (see *fig.* 17). The chromosomes that carry the gene or factor for red are here black, and those that carry the gene for white are white.

of the pairs of chromosomes are sorted out independently of each other (*fig. 37*). For example, in the cross between yellow-round and green-wrinkled peas, if one pair of chromosomes in the hybrid (F_1) carries the contrasted elements yellow and green and another pair of chromosomes of the same hybrid carries the round and wrinkled elements, then, if these chromosomes at the maturation period behave independently, there will be four kinds of germ-cells produced. These four kinds will carry a yellow-bearing and a round-bearing chromosome, or a yellow-bearing and a wrinkled-bearing chromosome, or a green-bearing and a round-bearing chromosome, or a green-bearing and a wrinkled-bearing chromosome.

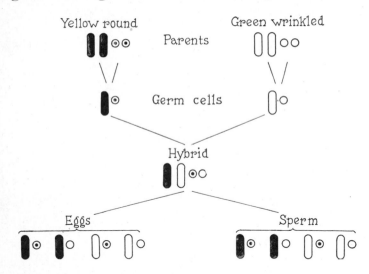

Fig. 37.—Diagram to illustrate the distribution of two pairs of chromosomes carrying two pairs of Mendelian factors, namely yellow-green and round-wrinkled. The chromosome carrying the gene for yellow is a black rod, that for green is a white circle; that carrying the gene for round is a circle with a dot, that for wrinkled is a circle without the dot.

Only these four kinds of germ-cells are possible on the chromosome mechanism. Self-fertilization of such a hybrid will give the same recombinations of chromosomes that Mendel's second law requires for the hereditary elements.

CHAPTER VII

THE LINKAGE GROUPS AND THE CHROMOSOMES

IF the hereditary elements, the genes, are carried by the chromosomes and if the chromosomes are persisting structures, there should be as many groups of hereditary characters as there are kinds of chromosomes. In only a few cases has a sufficient number of characters been studied to show whether there is any correspondence between the number of hereditary groups of characters and the number of chromosomes. In the vinegar fly, Drosophila, there are about four hundred characters that fall into four groups. On page 88 (*fig.* 38) some of these are given arranged according to groups. The characters are arranged in four groups, Group I, II, III and IV. Three of these groups are equally large or nearly so; Group IV contains only three characters. The characters are put into these groups because, in heredity, the members of each group tend to be inherited together, i.e., if two or more enter the cross together they tend to remain together through subsequent generations. On the other hand, any member of one group is inherited entirely independently of any member of the other groups; in the same way as Mendel's yellow-green pair of characters is inherited independently of the round-wrinkled pair.

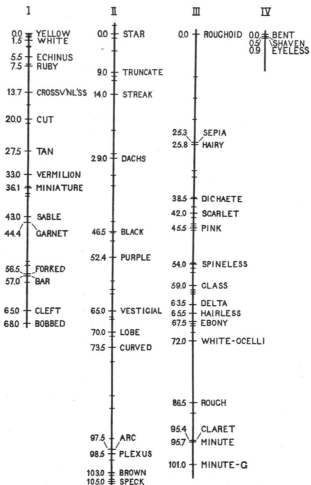

Fig. 38.—Chart of the genes of the chromosomes of Drosophila. The genes are arranged in the four linkage groups, I, II, III, IV. The name of the gene is given to the right of its locus, and the distance of the loci from one end of the chromosome is indicated by the numbers to the left of each locus. The "distance" gives the cross-over value for the genes corrected for double crossing-over.

In the chromosome group of Drosophila melanogaster (*fig.* 39) there are *four* pairs of chromosomes, three of nearly the same size and one much smaller. Not only is there agreement between the number of hereditary groups and the number of the chromo-

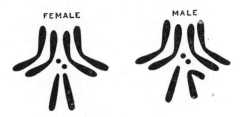

FEMALE   MALE

FIG. 39.—Female group and male group of chromosomes of Drosophila melanogaster.

somes, but even the size relations are the same, for there are three large groups of characters and three pairs of large chromosomes, and one small group of characters and one pair of small chromosomes.

The Four Linkage Groups of Drosophila Melanogaster

The following description of the characters of the wild fly may be useful in connection with the account of the modifications of these characters that appear in the mutants.

The head and thorax of the wild fly are grayish-yellow, the abdomen is banded with alternate stripes of yellow and black. In the male (*fig.* 6, left), there are three narrow bands and a black tip. In the female there are five black bands (*fig.* 6, right). The wings are gray with a surface texture of such a kind that at certain angles they are iridescent. The eyes are a deep, brick-red. The minute hairs that cover the body have a characteristic arrangement that is most obvious on the head and thorax. There is a definite number of larger hairs called bristles which have a characteristic position and are used for diagnostic purposes in classifying the species. On the foreleg of the male there is a comb-like organ formed by a row of bristles; it is absent in the female. The comb is a secondary sexual character.

Some of the characters of the mutant types are shown in *figures* 40, 41, 42, 43. The drawing of a single fly is often used here to illustrate more than one character. This is done to economize space, but of course there would be no difficulty in actually bringing together in the same individual any two or more characters belonging to the same group (or to different groups). Without colored figures it is not possible to show many of the most striking differences of these mutant races; at most, dark and light coloring can be indicated by the shading of the body, wings, or eyes.

GROUP I

The hereditary elements of this group are carried by the *X*-chromosomes. The characters are said to be sex-linked.

In the six flies drawn in *figure* 40 there are shown
five different wing characters. The first of these
types (*a*) is called cut, because the ends of the wings
look as though they had been cut to a point. The antennae are displaced downward and appressed and
their bristle-like aristae are crumpled.

The second figure (*b*) represents a fly with a
notch in the ends of the wings. This character is
dominant, but the same factor that produces the
notch in the wings is also a recessive lethal factor;
because of this latter effect of the character, no males
of this race exist, and the females of the race are
never pure but hybrid. This same figure (*b*) is used
here to show two other sex-linked characters. The

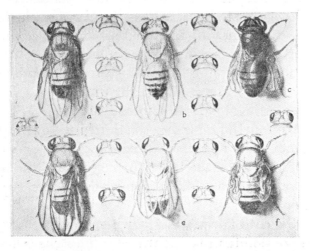

F<small>IG</small>. 40.—Some of the characters of the first chromosome of Drosophila melanogaster. See text.

spines on the thorax are twisted or kinky, which is due to a factor called "forked." The effect is best seen on the thorax, but all spines on the body are similarly modified; even the minute hairs are also affected. The lighter color of the body and antennae is intended to indicate that the character tan is also present. The tan flies are interesting because they have lost the positive heliotropism. As this peculiarity of the tan flies is inherited like all the other sex-linked characters, it follows that when a tan female is bred to a wild male all the sons inherit the recessive tan color and indifference to light, while the daughters show the dominant sex-linked character of their father, i.e., they are "gray," and go to the light. Hence when such a brood is disturbed the females fly to the light, but the males remain behind.

One of the first mutants that appeared was called rudimentary on account of the condition of the wings (c). The same mutation has appeared independently several times. In the drawing (c) the dark body color is intended to indicate "sable."

In the fourth figure (d) the third and fourth longitudinal veins of the wing are *fused* into one vein from the base of the wing to the level of the first cross-vein and in addition converge and meet near their outer ends.

In the fifth figure (e) the wings are shorter and more pointed than in the wild fly. This character is called miniature. The light color of the drawing may be taken to represent yellow body color.

In the last figure (*f*) of "club," the wings are pads, essentially in the same condition that they are in when the fly emerges from the pupa case. Not all the flies of this stock have the wings in this condition; some have fully expanded wings that appear normal in all respects. Nevertheless, about the same percentage of offspring show the pads irrespective of whether the parents had pads or expanded wings. The flies of this stock show, however, another character, which is a product of the same factor, and which is constant, i.e., repeated in all individuals. The two bristles on the sides of the thorax are constantly absent in this race.

There are many different eye colors in Group I, ranging from a pure white eye to vermilion, which could be shown only by the use of colored drawings.

GROUP II

The hereditary elements of members of Group II are carried by one pair of the two large bent chromosomes.

In the first drawing (*a*) of *figure* 41 which contains members of Group II, the wings are almost entirely absent or "vestigial." This condition arose at a single step and breeds true, although it appears to be influenced to some extent by temperature, also by modifiers that sometimes appear in the stock.

In the second figure (*b*) the wings turn up at the end. The mutant is called jaunty.

In the third figure (*c*) the wing is long and narrow and sometimes bent back on itself, as shown here. In several respects the wing resembles strap (*d*) but seems to be due to another factor, called antlered.

In the fourth figure (*d*) the wings are long and narrow and several of the veins are unrepresented. This character, "strap," is very variable. On the thorax there is a deep black mark called trefoil. In the

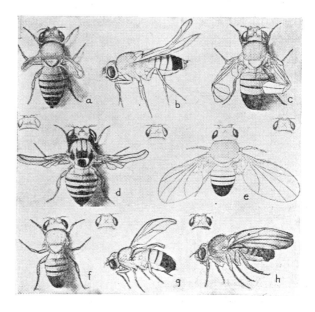

Fig. 41.—Some of the characters of the second chromosome of Drosophila melanogaster. See text.

wild fly there is a three-pronged mark on the thorax present in many individuals. Trefoil is a further development and modification of this mark and is due to a special factor.

The fifth figure (*e*) is called dachsoid; the body is shortened and the wings are broad and held out. The legs are short. The absence of cross-veins in the wings is characteristic.

In the sixth figure (*f*), apterous, the wings are entirely absent, not even the base remaining as in vestigial. The apterous flies are almost completely sterile.

The seventh figure (*g*) shows the wings "curved." In addition there is present a minute black speck at the base of each wing, due to another factor called speck.

In the eighth figure (*h*) the wings are arched. The factor is called arc. The dark color of the body, and especially of the wings, indicates the factor for black.

There are also a number of different eye colors in this group—one of which, brown, is darker in old flies than the red of the wild type.

GROUP III

The hereditary elements of Group III are carried by the other pair of large bent chromosomes.

In *figure* 42 (*a*), a mutant type called bithorax is shown. The old metathorax is replaced by another

mesothorax thrust in between the normal mesothorax and the abdomen. It carries a pair of wings
that do not completely unfold. On this new mesothorax the characteristic arrangement of the bristles
is shown. Thus at a single step a typical region of the
body has doubled. The character is recessive.

In the second figure (*b*) the dark color of the fly
is due to a factor called ebony.

The size of adult flies varies according to the
amount of nourishment obtained by the larva. After
the fly emerges its size remains nearly constant, as in
many insects. Two races have, however, been separated that are different in size as a result of a genetic
factor. The first of these, called dwarf, is represented
by *figure* 42 (*c*). The race is small but variable in
size, depending on food and other conditions. The
same figure shows the presence of another factor,
"sooty," that makes the fly dark.

In the fourth figure (*d*) another mutation in size
is shown. It is called "giant." The flies are twice the
size of wild flies.

In the fifth figure (*e*) the mutant dichaete is
shown. It is characterized by the absence of two of
the bristles on the thorax. Other bristles may also be
absent, but not so constantly as the two just mentioned. Another effect of the same factor is the
spread-out condition of the wings.

In the sixth figure (*f*) the wings are curled up
over the back; the character is called curled.

In the seventh figure (g) the wings are beaded, i.e., the margin is defective at intervals, giving a beaded-like outline to the wings. This condition is very variable and much affected by other factors that influence the shape of the wings.

There are many eye colors in this Group—one of

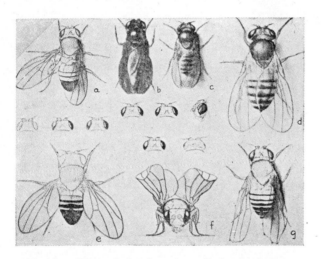

Fig. 42.—Some of the characters of the third chromosome of Drosophila melanogaster. See text.

these, sepia, becomes very dark in old flies. Pink and peach eye colors are modifications of the same gene (a case of multiple allelomorphs). Two other eye colors in this group, scarlet and cardinal, are almost indistinguishable, but the genes for these characters lie in quite different parts of the chromosome.

GROUP IV

The hereditary elements of Group IV are carried by the pair of very small chromosomes. Only three mutants have been obtained. One of these, called "eyeless" (*fig.* 43 *a, a¹*), is variable—the eyes are often entirely absent or represented by a few or by several ommatidia (*b, b¹*). On the sides of the head

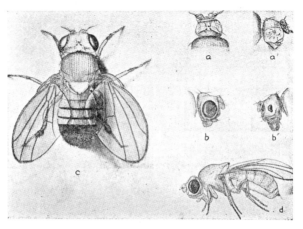

Fig. 43.—The three characters of the fourth chromosome of Drosophila melanogaster. See text.

where the normal eye lies there is, in "eyeless," a corresponding empty area in the more extreme condition (*a, a¹*), and even when a piece of the eye is present it lies in this area but failing to fill all of it, the outline of the full sized eye is, so to speak, still present. These parts of eyes (*b, b¹*) might be spoken of as rudimentary organs.

Drawing (c) in *figure* 43, represents "bent," so called from the shape of the wings. This mutant is likewise very variable, often indistinguishable from the wild type, yet when well developed strikingly different from any other mutant.

The third mutant (d) is called shaven. The bristles and hairs are extremely short, and the thorax especially, appears as though shaven.

This brief account of a few of the mutant races that can be most easily represented by uncolored figures will serve to show how all parts of the body may change, some of the changes being so slight that they would be overlooked except by an expert, others so great that the characters affected depart far from the original one.

It is important to note that the mutant genes in the X-chromosomes are not limited to any part of the body, nor do they affect more frequently a particular part. The same statement holds equally for all of the other chromosomes. In fact, since each factor may affect visibly several parts of the body at the same time there are no grounds for expecting any special relation between a given chromosome and special regions of the body. It cannot too insistently be urged that when we say a character is the product of a particular factor we mean no more than that it is the most conspicuous effect of that factor.

If, then, as these and other results to be described

point to the chromosomes as the bearers of the Mendelian factors, and if, as has been shown, these factors have a definite location in the chromosomes, it is clear that the location of the factors in the chromosomes bears no spatial relation to the architecture of the body.

CHAPTER VIII

SEX-LINKED INHERITANCE

When we follow the history of pairs of chromosomes we find that their distribution in successive generations is paralleled by the inheritance of Mendelian characters. This is best shown in the sex chromosomes (*fig.* 44). In the female of Drosophila there are two of these chromosomes that are called

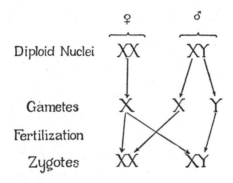

Fig. 44.—Diagram showing the distribution of the sex chromosomes from parents to offspring.

X-chromosomes; in the male there are also two, but one differs from those of the female in its shape, and in the fact that it carries none of the ordinary genetic factors. It is called the *Y*-chromosome.

The inheritance of a pair of characters whose genes lie in the *X*-chromosomes is shown in *figures*

45 and 46, illustrating crosses between a white-eyed and a red-eyed individual.

The first of these represents a cross between a white-eyed male and a red-eyed female (*fig.* 45, top row). The X-chromosome in the male is represented by a bar, (w), the Y-chromosome is bent. In the female the X-chromosomes are W and W. Each egg of such a female will retain one X (with W) after the polar bodies have been thrown off. In the male there are two classes of sperm—the female-producing, carrying X (with w); and the male-producing, carrying the Y-chromosome. Any egg fertilized by an X-bearing sperm will produce a female with red eyes, because the X-chromosome (W) from the mother carries the dominant factor for red. Any egg fertilized by a Y-bearing sperm will produce a male with red eyes because he gets his X-chromosome (W) from his mother.

When these two F_1 flies (second row) are inbred the following combinations are expected. Each egg will contain a red-eye producing X, (W), or a white-eye producing X, (w), after the polar bodies have been extruded. The male will produce two kinds of sperms, of which the female-producing will contain a red-eye producing X. Since any egg may by chance be fertilized by any sperm, there will be the four classes of individuals shown in the bottom row of the diagram. All the females will have red eyes, because irrespective of the two kinds

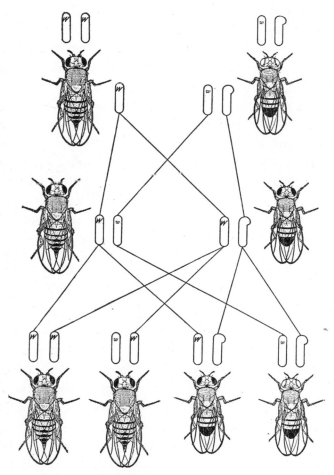

Fig. 45.—Cross of a red-eyed female and a white-eyed male of the vinegar fly, showing sex-linked inheritance.

of eggs of the female, all the female-producing sperm carry a (w) X. Half of the males have red eyes, because half of the eggs had each a red-producing X-chromosome. The other half of the males have white eyes, because half of the eggs had each a white-producing X-chromosome. Evidence from other sources shows that the Y-chromosome of the male is indifferent, so far as these Mendelian factors are concerned.

The reciprocal experiment is illustrated in *figure* 46. A white-eyed female is mated to a red-eyed male (top row). Each of the mature eggs of such a female contains one white-producing X-chromosome, represented by the open bar in the diagram. The red-eyed male contains female-producing X-bearing sperm, that carry the factor for red-eye color, and male-producing Y-chromosomes. Any egg fertilized by an X-bearing sperm will become a red-eyed female because the X-chromosome that comes from the father carries the dominant factor for red eye color. Any egg fertilized by a Y-bearing sperm will become a male with white eyes because the only X-chromosome that the male contains comes from his mother and is white-producing.

When these two F_1 flies are inbred (middle row) the following combinations are expected. Half the eggs will contain each a white-producing X-chromosome and half a red-producing. The female-producing sperms will each contain a white X- and the male-producing sperms will each contain an indifferent *Y*-chromosome. Chance meetings of eggs and sperms will give the four F_2 classes (bottom row). These

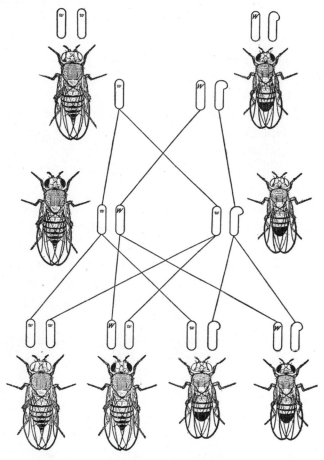

FIG. 46.—Cross of a white-eyed female and a red-eyed male of the vinegar fly, showing sex-linked inheritance.

consist of white-eyed and red-eyed females and white-eyed and red-eyed males. The ratio here is 1:1 and not three to one (3:1) as in other Mendelian cases. But Mendel's law of segregation is not transgressed, as the preceding analysis has shown; for, the chromosomes have followed strictly the course laid down on Mendel's principle for the distribution of factors. The peculiar result in this case is due to the fact that the F_1 male gets his single factor for eye color from his mother only, and it is contained in a body (the X-chromosome) that is involved in sex-determination, while the mate of this body, the Y-chromosome, is indifferent with regard to these factors.

In human inheritance there are characters that show this same kind of transmission. Color-blindness, or at least certain kinds of color-blindness, appears to follow the same scheme. A color-blind father transmits through his daughters his peculiarity to half of his grandsons, but to none of his granddaughters (fig. 69). The result is the same as in the case of the white-eyed male of Drosophila. Color-blind women are rather unusual, which is expected from the method of inheritance of this character, but in the few known cases where such color-blind women have married normal husbands all the F_1 sons inherit color-blindness from the mother (fig. 70). Here again the result is the same as for the similar combination in Drosophila.

In man the sex formula appears to be XX for the female and XO or XY for the male, and since this is essentially the same as that in Drosophila, the explanation of sex-linked inheritance is the same. According to de Winiwarter there are 48 chromosomes

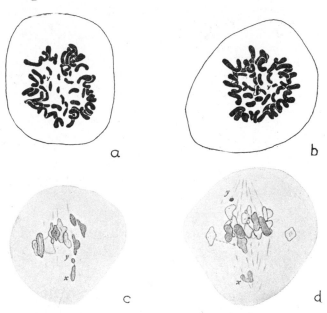

FIG. 47.—*a*, spermatogonium cell of white man, showing 48 chromosomes, including the small *Y*-chromosome; *b*, same of negro; *c* and *d*, Primary spermatocytes, side views, showing *X*- and *Y*-chromosomes. (*After Painter.*)

in the female and only 47 in the male, the Y-chromosome being absent. After the extrusion of the polar bodies there should be 24 left in the egg. In the male at one of the maturation divisions the single X-chromosome passes to one pole. In consequence there are two classes of sperms in man; female-producing containing 24 chromosomes, and male-producing containing 23 chromosomes. If the factor for color-

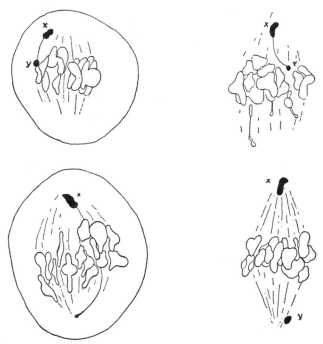

Fig. 48.—Primary spermatocytes of man, side views of spindle. The X- and the Y-chromosomes are separating in advance of the others. (*After Painter.*)

blindness is carried by the X-chromosome its inheritance in man works out on the same chromosome scheme and in the same way as does white eye color (or any other sex-linked character) in Drosophila, for the O-sperm in man would be equivalent to the Y-sperm in the fly.

Painter's later evidence (*fig.* 47), showing that there is a small Y-chromosome in the male that acts as the mate of the X-chromosome (*fig.* 48), is very convincing. Whether in man the male is XO or XY the explanation of sex-linked inheritance is the same since the factors involved are carried by the X-chromosomes.

CHAPTER IX

CROSSING-OVER

IF the linkage were never broken we should expect to find that groups of characters would be inherited together. There would be as many such groups of characters as there are pairs of chromosomes. To a certain extent this is true, but the study of the inheritance of two or more characters in the same linkage group has revealed a further fact of great interest, namely, that there takes place an interchange at times between the two members of the same linkage group, and, it may be added, only between members of the same linkage group and never between different linkage groups. This interchange gives rise to a new phenomenon in inheritance that is called crossing-over, which may be illustrated by a few typical examples from Drosophila.

There are two mutant characters, black body color and vestigial wings, whose genes lie in the second chromosome. If a fly having these two characters is crossed to a wild type fly with normal color and long wings (*fig.* 49) the offspring are like wild type flies, because normal dominates black and long wing dominates vestigial wing.

If one of the daughters (F_1) from this cross is now mated to a male with black color and vestigial wings (both recessive characters) the offspring are

of four kinds. Two of these are like the grandparents, one black-vestigial, the other normal-long,
but the other two kinds have, as it were, interchanged

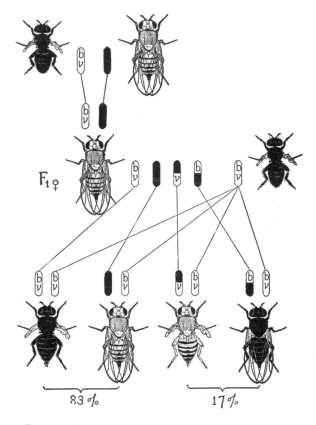

Fig. 49.—Diagram to illustrate crossing-over. The two
mutant characters, black and vestigial, are linked, as are
their normal allelomorphs, gray and long. A black vestigial
male is mated to a gray long female. The F_1 female is
back-crossed to the double recessive type, black vestigial.
Four kinds of offspring are produced.

these characteristics. One kind is black-long, the other normal-vestigial.

These four kinds do not appear in equal numbers, but 83 per cent are like the grandparents and 17 per cent are the cross-overs. The result may be stated in another way. The mutant characters that went in together, black-vestigial and normal-long, have remained together (linked) in 83 per cent of the grandchildren, while in 17 per cent of the grandchildren there has been an interchange or crossing-over.

The results may be represented in terms of chromosomes as follows. The gene for black is represented by b and its normal partner by B; the gene for vestigial by v and its partner by V (*fig.* 49). Black (b) and vestigial (v) are represented in the figure as contained in the same chromosome (here a rod) in one parent, and gray (B) and long wing (V) by the corresponding chromosome in the other parent, here by the all-black chromosome. The daughter contains one of each of these two chromosomes. When her eggs mature these two chromosomes separate and some of the eggs contain one, some the other chromosome. These two kinds of eggs as the sequel shows represent 83 per cent of all the eggs. But in 17 per cent of the cases there has occurred in some way an interchange between these two chromosomes with the result that the genes for black and long come to be in one chromosome and normal and vestigial in the other. The genes for black and normal may be said to have crossed over.

When such a female is mated to a black-vestigial male, whose spermatozoa contain the chromosome with black and vestigial, four combinations are formed. Remembering that normal dominates black, and long dominates vestigial, it will be seen (*fig.* 49) that four kinds of offspring are expected.

A second case of crossing over, here in the *X*-chromosome, is illustrated in *figure* 50.

If a female with white eyes and yellow wings is crossed to a wild male with red eyes and gray wings, the sons are yellow and have white eyes and the daughters are gray and have red eyes. If two F_1 flies are mated they will produce the following classes:

Yellow	Gray	Yellow	Gray
White	Red	Red	White
98.5%		1.5%	

Not only have the two grandparental combinations reappeared, but in addition two new combinations, viz., gray-white and yellow-red. The two original combinations far exceed in numbers the new or exchange combinations. If we follow the history of the *X*-chromosomes we find that the *larger classes* of grandchildren can be explained if *X*-chromosomes are transmitted in their entirety from one generation to the next.

The *smaller classes* of grandchildren, the exchange combinations or cross-overs, can be explained by an interchange taking place between the chromosomes in the hybrid (F_1) female. This is indicated in the diagram.

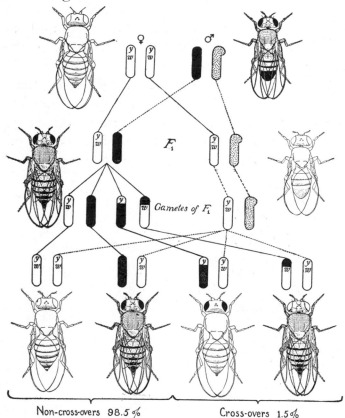

Non-cross-overs 98.5%   Cross-overs 1.5%

Fig. 50.—Cross of a female vinegar fly that has white eyes and yellow wings to a wild type male with red eyes and gray wings, illustrating crossing-over.

The explanation of crossing-over rests on the assumption that members of the same pair of chromosomes may at times interchange. If the chromosomes are the bearers of the genes there can be no doubt from the genetic evidence that such an interchange takes place. When we turn to the known behavior of the chromosomes in the ripening of the germ cells we find certain stages where such a process may seem possible.

At the ripening period of the germ cell the members of each pair of chromosomes come together. In several forms they have been described as meeting at one end and then progressively coming to lie side by side as shown in *figure 51*. At the completion of

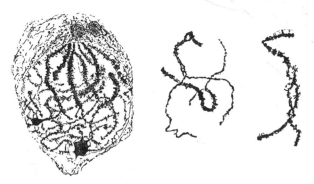

Fig. 51.—Conjugation of the chromosomes in Batracoceps. (*After Janssens.*)

the process they appear to have united along their length. It is always a maternal and a paternal chromosome that meet in this way and always two of the

same kind. It has been observed that as the members
of a pair come together they occasionally twist
around each other (*fig.* 51). If where they overlap
they should break and the ends unite with the corresponding ends of the opposite chromosomes (*fig.*
52), the conditions of crossing-over would be fulfilled.

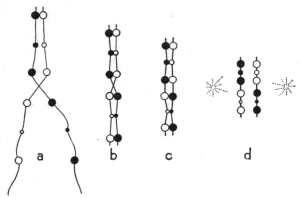

FIG. 52.—Diagram to illustrate crossing-over of two conjugating threads.

Unfortunately the evidence that crossing-over
takes place at the time of maturation, as the result of
overlapping of the chromosomes, is very meagre and
by no means conclusive, nevertheless, as far as it
goes, this evidence is favorable for such an interpretation of genetic crossing-over as that given above.

From the genetic evidence for crossing-over it is
possible to determine the relative location of the
genes in the chromosomes. The method can not be
given here in detail but the general point of view

may be stated. If the genes lie along the length of the chromosomes and if crossing-over is as likely to occur at one level as at another, then, the nearer together two genes lie the less likely is a break be- tween them, or conversely the further apart in the chromosome they lie the more likely is crossing-over to take place. In other words the percentage of crossovers is an index of the distance apart of the genes. On this basis the location of the genes, as shown in *figure* 38, has been determined. From such a chart one is enabled to calculate what the inher- itance of any gene will be with respect to any other gene in its group provided its relation to two other genes is known.

The theory of crossing-over enables the geneticist to predict the results of a given experiment with the same precision that Mendel's two laws allow predic- tion for a single pair of characters in the same chro- mosome pair, or for two or more pairs of characters in different chromosome pairs.

Chapter X
NATURAL SELECTION AND EVOLUTION

DARWIN's Theory of Natural Selection still holds today first place in every discussion of evolution, and for this reason the theory calls for careful scrutiny; for it is not difficult to show that the expression "natural selection" is to many men a metaphor that carries many meanings, and sometimes different meanings to different men. While I heartily agree with my fellow biologists in ascribing to Darwin himself, and to his work, the first place in evolutionary philosophy, yet recognition of this claim should not deter us from a careful analysis of the situation in the light of all that has been done since Darwin's time.

The Theory of Natural Selection

In his famous book on the *Origin of Species,* Darwin tried to do two things: first, to show that the theory of evolution furnishes an adequate explanation of the facts. No such great body of evidence had ever been brought together before, and it convinced most thinking men that the theory of evolution of living things furnished a rational explanation of what is known about their relationships and past history.

Darwin also proposed several theories as to how

evolution has taken place. He pointed to the influence of the environment, to the effects of use and disuse, and to natural selection. It is to the last theory that his name is especially attached. He appealed to a fact familiar to everyone, that no two individuals are identical and that some of the differences that they show are inherited. He argued that those individuals that are best suited to their environment are the most probable ones to survive and to leave offspring. As a consequence, their descendants should in time replace through competition the less well-adapted individuals of the species. This is the process Darwin called natural selection, and Spencer called the survival of the fittest.

Stated in these general terms there is nothing in the theory to which anyone is likely to take exception; for, it may appear little more than a truism to state that the individuals that are the best adapted to survive have a better chance of surviving than those not so well adapted to survive. But Darwin did much more than appeal to any such generality. He pointed out that variations occur in all directions; that at least some of these variations are transmitted; and that on an average more offspring are produced by each pair than survive. He appealed directly to a large amount of biological evidence in support of his theory.

Since 1859 a great deal of work has been done that bears on the interpretation that Darwin placed on the facts to which he appealed. Before deciding on the merits of natural selection this evidence must be examined.

The Measurement of Variation

If we measure, or weigh, or classify any character shown by the individuals of a population, we find much variability some of which we ascribe to the varied experiences that the individuals have encountered in the course of their lives, i.e., to their environment, but we also recognize that some of the differences may be due to individuals having different inheritances. A few familiar examples will help to bring out this contrast.

If the leaves of a tree are arranged according to size (*fig. 53*), we find a continuous series, but there

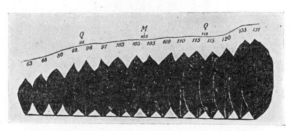

Fig. 53.—Series of leaves of a tree arranged according to size. (*After DeVries.*)

are more leaves of medium size than extremes. If a lot of beans be sorted out according to their weights, and those between certain weights put into cylinders, the cylinders, when arranged according to the size of the beans, will appear as shown in *figure* 54. An imaginary line running over the tops of the piles will give a curve (*fig.* 55) that corresponds to the curve of probability (*fig.* 56).

Fig. 54.—Beans put into cylinders according to size of beans. The cylinders are arranged according to the size of the contained beans. (*After DeVries.*)

If we stand men in lines according to their height we get a similar arrangement.

The differences in size shown by the individual beans or by the individual men are due in part to heredity, in part to the environment in which they have developed. This is a familiar fact of almost every-day observation. It is well shown in the following example. In *figure 57* the two boys and the two varieties of corn, which they are holding, differ in height. The pedigrees of the boys (*fig.* 58) make it probable that their height is partly inherited, and

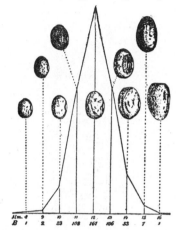

Fig. 55.—A curve resulting from arrangement of beans according to size. (*After DeVries.*)

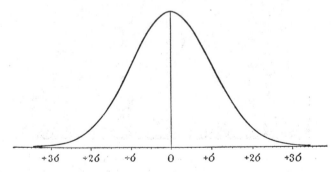

Fig. 56.—Curve of probability. (*After Johannsen.*)

the two races of corn are known to belong to a tall
and a short race respectively. Here, then, the chief
effect or difference is due to heredity. On the other
hand, if individuals of the same race develop in a

Fig. 57.—A short and a tall boy, each holding a stalk
of corn. The short boy holds a stalk of a race of short corn,
and the tall boy one of tall corn. (*After Blakeslee.*)

favorable environment the result is different from
what their development would be in an unfavorable
environment (*fig.* 59). Here to the right the corn is
crowded and in consequence dwarfed, while to the

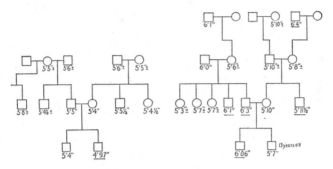

Fig. 58.—Pedigrees of boys shown in fig. 57.

Fig. 59.—Corn raised under different conditions. That to the
left is spaced, that to the right is crowded. (*After Blakeslee.*)

left the same kind of corn has had more room to develop and is taller.

Darwin knew that if selection of particular kinds of individuals of a population takes place the next generation is affected. If the taller men of a community are selected, *the average* of their offspring will be taller than the average of the former population. If selection for tallness again takes place, still taller men will *on the average* arise. If selection again makes a choice, the process may continue (*fig.* 60).

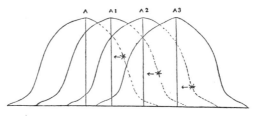

Fig. 60.—Curves showing (hypothetically) how selection might be supposed to bring about progress in the direction of selection. (*After Goldschmidt.*)

Now while we recognize that this statement contains an important truth, it has been found that it contains only a part of the truth. Any one who repeats for himself this kind of selection experiment will find that while the average class will often at first change in the direction of selection, the process slows down as a rule rather suddenly (*fig.* 61). He finds, moreover, that the limits of variability are not necessarily transcended as the process con-

tinues even although the average may for a while
be increased. More tall men may be produced by
selection of this kind, but the tallest men are not
necessarily any taller than the tallest in the original
population.

Selection, then, has not produced anything new,
but only more of certain kinds of individuals. Evolution, however, means producing new things, not
more of what already exists.

Darwin's interpretation as to the effect of con-

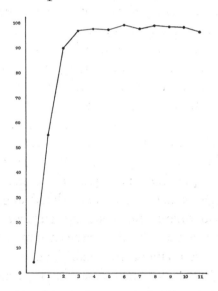

Fig. 61.—Diagram ilustrating the results of selecting for extra bristles in
Drosophila melanogaster. Selection at
first produces rapid effects, which soon
slow down and then cease. (*After
MacDowell.*)

tinued selection in the same direction may seem to
imply that the range of variation shown by the offspring of a given individual about that type of individual would be as wide as the range shown by the
original population, but Galton's work first made
clear that this is not the case in a general or mixed
population. If the offspring of individuals did continue to show as wide a range of variability about the
new average as did the original population, then it
would follow that selection could slide successive
generations along in the direction of selection.

Darwin himself was extraordinarily careful, however, in the statements he made in this connection, and
it is rather by implication than by actual reference
that one can ascribe this meaning to his views. Some
of his contemporaries and many of his followers,
however, appear to have accepted this *sliding scale*
interpretation as the cardinal doctrine of evolution.
And in this connection we should not forget that just
this sort of process was supposed to take place in the
inheritance of use and disuse. What is gained in one
generation forms the basis for further gains in the
next generation. Now, Darwin not only believed
that acquired characters are inherited but turned
more and more to this explanation in his later writings. Let us, however, not make too much of the
matter; for it is not so important to find out whether
Darwin's ideas were as definite on this point as our
own as it is to make sure that our own ideas are clear

in the light of the more recent and extensive studies
of variation that have been made since Darwin's
time.

Selection and Variation

If, then, all that selection can do is to produce
more individuals of a given type, it may appear that
this part of Darwin's evidence fails to support his
assumption that the observed variability of animals
and plants suffices to furnish selection with its necessary material. It is here that the mutation theory
has a contribution to make. Since 1900 much evidence has been obtained showing that new variations
may appear that transcend the extremes of variation of the original type. These, if they are inherited,
are called mutants. In some cases the new type so
far transcends the original type that the extreme
fluctuations of the two do not overlap; but in other
cases the new type may be nearer to the original one
and the fluctuations of each may overlap.

Darwin knew of cases of sudden mutation and
called them sports or monstrosities. He thought that
they could seldom supply materials for evolution
because they changed a part so greatly as to throw
the organism as a whole out of harmony with its
environment. This argument for rejecting extreme
or monstrous forms seems to us today as valid as it
did to Darwin; but we now recognize that sports are
only extreme types of mutation, and that even the

smallest changes that add to or subtract from a part
in the smallest measurable degree may also arise
by mutation. We identify these smaller mutational
changes as the most probable variants that make a
theory of evolution possible both because they do
transcend the original types, and because they are
inherited. If there are other kinds of heritable variations than mutants, it seems scarcely possible that they
should have been overlooked; for, many thorough-
going studies of variation have now been made.

Pure Lines

The work of the Danish botanist, Johannsen, published in 1909, furnishes the most critical evidence relating to the inheritance of variations that has as yet
been obtained. There are, moreover, special reasons
why the material that he used is better suited to give
definite information than any other so far studied.

Johannsen worked with a garden bean (Phaseolus
vulgaris nana), weighing the seeds or else measur-
ing them. The plant multiplies by self-fertilization.
Taking advantage of this fact Johannsen kept the
seeds of each plant separate from the others, and
raised from them a new generation. When curves
were made of these new groups it was found that
some of them had different modes from that of the
original general population (*fig.* 62, *A-E*, bottom
group). They are shown in the upper groups (*A, B,*

C, D, E). The general population is a composite of all the groups.

That his conclusion is correct is shown by rearing

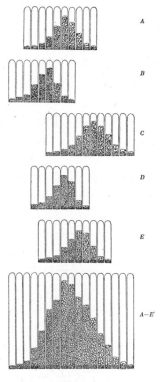

I

Fig. 62.—Pure lines of beans. The lower figure (A-E) gives the general population, the figures above give the pure lines within the population. (*After Johannsen.*)

a new generation from one plant or indeed from several plants of any one of these lines. Each line repeats the same modal class. There is no further breaking up into groups. Within the line it does not matter at all whether one chooses a big bean or a little one—they will give the same result. In a word, the germ-material in each of these lines is pure, or homozygous, as we say. The differences that are found between the weights (or sizes) of the individual beans are due to their location in the pod or in the plant on which they have developed.

Johannsen's work shows that the frequency distribution of a pure line is due to factors that are extrinsic to the germ-plasm. It does not matter then which individuals in a pure line are used to breed from, for they all carry the same germ-material.

We can now understand more clearly how selection acting on a general population brings about, at first, changes in the direction of selection.

An individual is picked out from the population in order to test its particular kind of germ-material. Although the different classes of individuals may overlap, so that one can not always judge an individual from its appearance, nevertheless, on the whole, chance favors the picking out of the kind of germ-material sought. In species with separate sexes there is the further difficulty that two individuals must be chosen for each mating, and superficial examination of them does not insure that they

belong to the same group—their germ-plasm cannot
be inspected. Hence selection of biparental forms is
a precarious process, now going forward, now back-
wards, now standing still. In time, however, the process forward is almost certain to take place provided
the selection is from a heterogeneous population.
Johannsen's work was simplified because he started
with pure lines. In fact were this not the case his
work would not have been essentially different from
that of any other selection experiment.

It has since been pointed out by Jennings and by
Pearl that a race that reproduces by self-fertilization,
as does this bean, automatically becomes pure in all
of the factors that make up its germ-material. Since
self-fertilization is the normal process in this bean
the purity of the germ-plasm of each line already
existed when Johannsen began to experiment.

Genetic Variability

In addition to the variability due to external factors acting on the individual during its development
there are also differences in the germ-materials—
genetic factors—that are known to produce slight
differences in the extent to which some particular
part or character develops. Inasmuch as some of
these minor or modifying genetic factors produce
their results only in the presence of the chief character, they may be concealed and only manifest their
presence when the chief character develops. The

discovery of the occurrence of such modifying genetic factors has gone a long way in making clear
some of the effects of selection—effects that have at
times led some of the neo-Darwinians to assume that
the selection process could bring about a change that
causes the organisms to transcend its original type.

Castle stated in 1916: "Many students of genetics
at present regard unit characters as unchangeable.
. . . For several years I have been investigating
this question, and the general conclusion at which I
have arrived is this, that unit characters are modifi-
able as well as recombinable. Many Mendelians
think otherwise but this is, I believe, because they
have not studied the question closely enough. The
fact is unmistakable that unit characters are subject to quantitative variation." That Castle was not
carelessly playing fast and loose with the term factor
(gene) and character is shown by the whole con-
text of the entire chapter in which this sentence
occurs. It is intended to be understood to mean that
unit characters may not only be altered by the recombination of modifying characters, for, Castle
has always recognized this possibility, but also
that the gene (factor) varies quantitatively and that
selection not only produces its results by selecting
larger or smaller genes but in doing so it brings
about progressive and further advances in the direction of selection. This interpretation is attributed by
Castle to Darwin himself, as another quotation from

the same chapter shows: "Selection as an agency in evolution must then be restored to the important place which it held in Darwin's estimation, an agency capable of producing continuous and progressive racial changes."

Now the only really critical piece of work done on this subject, that of Johannsen, had already led to the opposite result. It can hardly be said, therefore, that the subject had not been studied closely enough. The evidence from Castle's own experiments with hooded rats when studied more critically has shown that it still remains to be proven that genes are subject to quantitative variations and are amenable to selection.

Conclusions

The evidence discussed in this chapter is consistent with the view that the individual gene is not affected by selection, and that the initial changes commonly observed when selection is practised on a mixed population are due to recombinations of the different kinds of genes affecting the same character that are present in most populations. Since these modifying genes behave in inheritance strictly in accordance with Mendel's laws there are no grounds for assuming that they are different from other genes. Selection ceases to produce any further effects after these genes have been sorted out and the material has become homozygous for them.

It follows, that if new characters transcending the extremes of the original population arise, this must come about through a change in one or more of the genes themselves. At present we have discovered only one way in which such a change takes place— by a mutation in a gene.

CHAPTER XI
THE ORIGIN OF SPECIES BY NATURAL SELECTION

THE question still remains whether under natural selection the mutational changes that appear sporadically will suffice to supply the materials for new species. Genetics has shown that in all probability only one gene of a pair mutates at a time. If the mutation occurs late in the history of the germ-cells, the mutated gene might be retained in an egg or in two sperm-cells. If the mutation occurred earlier in the germ track the mutated gene might, if in a female, remain in several eggs after the polar bodies are formed, or if in a male, remain in many sperm-cells. If a germ-cell carrying the new gene happens to combine with a germ-cell of another *normal* individual, the cells of the embryo so produced will contain the gene in only one of its chromosomes, and such an individual will not show the character if the gene is recessive. In this individual, half of the mature germ-cells will now contain the gene and half its normal partner. If such an individual mates with a normal individual, half of its offspring will carry the gene in only one chromosome of each cell. Here, for the first time, the new gene is present in many individuals—in half as many as are produced by the mating. This process may by chance be repeated over and over again, but sooner or later two individuals each carrying the gene may mate. One-fourth of their offspring will then show the new character, which now appears for the first time. Several or many mutant individuals will then suddenly emerge, and since they are the output of the same female, their proximity will increase the chance that two at least mate with each other and produce progeny with the new character.

These considerations are significant for the selection theory. They show that there is no danger of a new mutant being lost at its inception, except in so far as chance works against the survival of the off-spring of any one individual. They show also that a new gene may, by chance, become distributed in the race before its character comes to the surface. If, when it appears, the new character is one that better fits the individuals to some environment at hand, such individuals have a better chance of survival and, other things being equal, of leaving offspring. If one of them mates with an individual of the original race the same process takes place all over again, but as often as this happens, the new gene may spread in the race at the expense of the old, and may replace it if the character it stands for is one better suited to the old environment; or, if better fitted to a new environment within reach, it will then give rise to a new type leaving the original type in possession of the old station.

The integrity of a new gene protects it from being lost through crossing with the old type, because there is no blending of the gene with the original one each time the two are brought together. Darwin confused here the characters that may blend in the hybrid with the genes that do not blend. The maintenance of the gene's integrity overcomes a serious difficulty in Darwin's theory of natural selection as he first formulated it.

Soon after the appearance of the *Origin,* Fleming Jenkin—a Scotch engineer—pointed out that single variants would disappear by "swamping" even although slightly beneficial, if, as Darwin supposed, blended inheritance is the rule after crossing; for, the new character will lose some of its advantage each time it combines with the original type. The chance is always greater, at first, of a mating with an individual of the original type owing to the larger numbers of such individuals. In later editions of the *Origin* Darwin acknowledged the force of this objection and tried to meet it by postulating that the new character must be already present in a large number of individuals if it is going to have anything like a chance of survival. But one may ask if a *new* adaptive character can appear in so large a number of individuals that it swamps virtually the original type, what becomes of the theory of natural selection? If the adaptive change has already taken place in so many individuals it is simpler to assume that it might soon appear in all as the result of whatever change induced its appearance in so many.

Now this dilemma is to some extent at least met by the modern theory of the stability of the gene. A gene is not lost by residing in the same cell with a gene of another kind. It may, if mere chance favors its perpetuation, spread, and once inoculated in the race it may produce in time enough individuals to start a new type. Our modern knowledge of the behavior of the gene meets to some extent the difficulty raised by Fleming Jenkin and reestablishes the strength of Darwin's theory, but, on the other hand, it should be clearly understood that the chance of a recessive gene becoming widely disseminated is extremely small even though the character it represents may be a beneficial one.

The stability of the gene also enables us to understand how a gene, if it is recessive, representing a character that is even injurious to the race, may become spread, locally at least, in a group without detriment to the individuals carrying one gene. This explains the frequent occurrence, in certain restricted populations, of the appearance at times of certain abnormal types, as seen, for instance, in night blindness, and "bleeding" in man.

There is another result, clearly established by the genetic work on Drosophila, that is favorable to the final establishment of a new type or character if it is beneficial. Most, perhaps all, of the mutations appear more than once. This improves their chances of becoming incorporated in the species, and if the mutation produces a character that favors survival the chance of its becoming established is still further increased. But it is also not to be overlooked that since most of these mutational changes are not beneficial, their recurrence acts as a drag on the race, because in so far as their genes become disseminated they give rise to defective individuals whenever two such genes are brought together. The early death of defective individuals in the wild state may make their appearance less noticeable than under the more favorable conditions for survival under domestication.

It is sometimes implied that a mutational change that is dominant has a better chance than a recessive. This is not the case, however, if the dominant character is neither advantageous nor injurious, but neutral. It, then, has the same chance as a recessive. But if the dominant is beneficial, it has a somewhat better chance than a recessive, because, since it comes to expression from the beginning in the hybrid type, it improves the chances of that type in comparison with the original type. If the dominant is injurious it will be more quickly eliminated than a recessive character that is injurious.

These theoretical considerations do no more than suggest certain possibilities concerning the theory of natural selection. Before we can judge as to its actual efficiency we must be able to state how much

of a given advantage each change must add to give
it a chance to become established in a population of
a given number. Since only relatively few of the individuals produced in each generation become the
parents of future generations, numbers count heav-
ily against any one individual establishing itself.
This is a most difficult problem for which we have
practically no data, and as yet only the beginning
of a theoretical analysis has been made of this side of
the selection problem. Haldane has developed a partial analysis of the problem for a few Mendelian sit-
uations. He points out that the problem is extremely
complex and that there is at present not much quantitative information to furnish material for such a
study of natural selection by means of gene mutations.

The Diagnostic Characteristics of Species and the Origin of Species by Natural Selection

It has often been pointed out that the characters
used by systematists to separate species have as a
rule nothing whatsoever to do with the adaptive fea-
tures of species. The latter are largely physiological.
Yet if species have originated through adaptive
modifications, it might be expected that physiological characters would be the most distinctive ones
that distinguish species from one another.

The solution of this paradox is, I think, to be
found in the many-sided effects produced by each
gene. It has been shown, particularly clearly in the

mutant types of Drosophila, that visible, superficial changes are nearly always accompanied by other changes that have a more physiological aspect, such as the vigor, or length of life, or productivity of the individual. From the point of view of evolution these physiological effects are those of most significance, while the superficial changes are trivial in comparison.

Now it is highly probable, if definite structural changes have definite accompanying physiological changes, that other mutations that bring about physiological changes produce, at the same time, superficial structural effects. If so, we may find here an explanation of the constancy of the latter when they are by-products of important physiological characters. Hence their constancy and their value as diagnostic characters of species.

The study of the mutation process has to a large extent also concerned itself with superficial characters, while the concomitant physiological modifications are referred to only in passing; but from the evolutionist's point of view it is the internal physiological accompaniments of the superficial effects that are of much greater significance. It is not surprising, therefore, that a good deal of the discussion of the bearing of mutants on the theory of evolution may seem rather far afield. If the mutation process were studied as contributory to the theory of evolution rather than in its genetic bearings we would reverse our present attitude and study minutely the effects of each new gene on the changes that it brings about in the life of the individual and on its productivity. We would then regard the superficial characters as by-products of the invisible effects, unimportant in themselves and at best only indices of internal modifications.

Chance and Evolution

When we consider the innumerable physiological adjustments of any organism, and the many structural adjustments of the parts of the body to each other and to the environment, an appeal to evolution through chance variation may seem preposterous. Stated in this general way the theory of evolution by chance variations seems repellent to the traditional thinking of many persons. It is this supposed difficulty, I think, that has driven some biologists and laymen, either to the acceptance of some sort of external guiding principle responsible for evolution, or to the assumption of an internal mystical property (entelechy) of living things, or to the cruder appeal to the inheritance of acquired characters. There is, however, a well known property of living organisms that puts the theory of chance, as the sufficient agent in evolution, on a very different footing from chance as generally understood. This is the property of living things to multiply their kind indefinitely, i.e., to reproduce an indefinitely

large number of individuals with the stamp of a
lucky throw. For example, no one would maintain
that so complex a mechanism as that of a living organism could suddenly appear by the accidental
coming together of the materials of which it is at
present composed. This is as inconceivable as that
an automobile could develop through the chance
meeting of wood, iron, rubber, oil, and gasoline; or
to use Paley's old image, that a watch could be produced by the accidental accumulation of pieces of
iron. The parts of the automobile and of the watch
have been brought together under the direction of a
human agent, but what has brought the parts of the
organism together? The implication in this question
is that there must have been a directing agent of
some sort, since by chance such a fortuitous combination is inconceivable. The statement ignores
certain properties of living materials that put the
two problems in a different light. These are the
property of growth by which living matter can increase indefinitely in volume; the property of mul-
tiplication by which a given sample may duplicate
itself without limit; and the possibility of changes
in the material that furnish new stable conditions.
We may not be able at present to explain fully how
growth takes place, but there is nothing in growth,
as far as known, that is inconsistent with chemical
processes. We may not be able to state in detail how
cells divide, but the purely physical character of the

process can scarcely be doubted. We may not be able to give the cause of a new variation, but we find nothing in the occurrence of a change that produces a variation that is inconsistent with chemical or structural alterations in the germ material. If this much be conceded, the problem of self-construction of even a complicated piece of mechanism is not beyond our comprehension. At any rate the problem is obviously different in kind from that of constructing a mechanism whose materials do not possess these properties. So long as the processes of division and growth take place faster than the process of accidental destruction or death, the living material can maintain itself indefinitely. The stability of such an organism is no greater, of course, than that of the chemical material of which it is composed. If this changes in those parts that have the property of division and growth (without affecting these properties) something new will result, a new type, and if this is able to maintain itself we can imagine at least something new may be established. It is not necessary to suppose that all changes will have a survival value, but only that some of them may. The alteration may bring the organism into a new relation with its environment, or through competition with the old type replace it, or it may make it possible for the new type to move into an environment different from that of the original type and hence escape competition.[1] Such a process may or may not lead to greater complexity, but would be an evolutionary change in any case. It should not be overlooked that only a limited number of living things are relatively complicated structures. An immense world of apparently simple organisms exists on the earth at the present time. Evolution has not meant the substitution of the simpler by the more complex; both exist side by side today, each standing in a different relation to the environment, but neither more capable of remaining in existence than the other.

The phrase natural selection, or its equivalent, the survival of the fittest, is generally understood to mean that a new type that appears, being better adapted to the same environment, displaces the old type by competition. One new "species" replaces its parent species. Something new has evolved, and by implication something "better," i.e., something with better chances of survival than the original species. While such replacement of an old type by a new one through competition may be one of the ways that new types evolve, it would be erroneous to suppose that Darwin limited the term in this way. It would be unfortunate to identify selection with such an

---

[1] The situation is essentially the same if the new type is fitted to establish a new relation with a different part of the same original environment—as when birds developed wings to take advantage of the air. Such a change may, it is true, lead through competition to a substitution of the new for the old type, but at other times it may also remove the new from competition with the old type. Birds for example have not replaced lizards.

interpretation. Darwin by no means restricted the application of the term natural selection to the substitution for the parent type of a better adapted new type. Perhaps it is owing to the various ways in which he used natural selection—often as a metaphor—that it has come to have so many different meanings and is often confusedly used as synonymous with evolution.

Progressive Evolution

It has been pointed out that the power to reproduce itself puts the problem of the construction of a living organism on a different footing from the construction of a complex machine out of inorganic (not living) material. This question is so important for the theory of evolution that its significance must be further indicated.

Whenever a variation in a new direction becomes established the chance of further advance in the same direction is increased. An increase in the number of individuals possessing a particular character has an influence on the future course of evolution,— not because the new type is more likely to mutate again in the same direction, but because a mutation in the same direction has a better chance of producing a further advance since all individuals are now on a higher level than before. When, for example, elephants had trunks less than a foot long (*fig.* **63**) the chance of getting trunks more than one foot

FIG. 63.—Evolution of elephant's trunk; above Maeritherium, in the middle Tetrabelodon (*After Lancaster*); below African elephant (*After Gambier Bolton*).

long would be in proportion to the length of the trunks already present and to the number of individuals in which such a character might appear. In other words, evolution once begun in a given direction is in a favorable position to go on in the same direction rather than in another (*fig.* 64), so long as

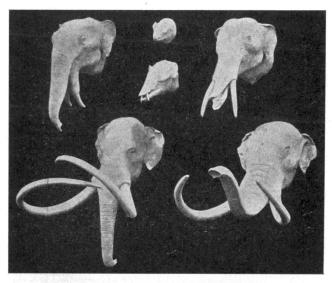

Fig. 64.—Evolution of elephant's trunk. (*After Lull.*)

the advance does not overstep the limit where further change is advantageous.

The duality of the evolution process from the point of view of natural selection has not always been sufficiently emphasized. A series of events that can be given a strictly causal interpretation leads

to the occurrence of a new individual, which, through
other properties inherent in living matter, can reproduce a group of individuals like itself. Another
and entirely unconnected series of events in the
outer world has produced another situation as when
the land was lifted above the water. If the new type
happens to come into relation with the new world
it may perpetuate itself there. This is adaptation—
the fortuitous coming together of the results of two
processes that have developed independently of each
other. The fitness of the animal or plant to an environment that it finds existing, gives the false impression that its relation to the environment, its
adaptation, has come about through a response to
the environment. The central idea of natural selection, as generally understood at the present time, is
that the relation is purely fortuitous. The organism
has been produced by one series of events, the environment by another; the relation of the two is
secondary.

The Dominance of the Wild Type Genes

The genes that arise by mutation have been found
to be largely recessive to the genes already present
in the original type which are said, therefore, to be
dominant to the new genes. If the original genes also
arose by mutation there is no obvious reason why
new genes are not as often dominant as recessive to
the original ones. It may be frankly admitted that

at present we cannot give a satisfactory explanation
of this relation if we assume that evolution has come
about by the same kind of processes that we observe
today when new mutants arise. There are, however,
certain considerations that put the situation in a
somewhat different light.

In the first place there is no such sharp contrast
as implied in the statement just made between dominant and recessive genes. Many genes classified as
recessive produce some effect in hybrid combination
on the character most affected.

In the second place if recessive mutant genes may
sometimes revert to the original type (for which
there is some evidence at present but not enough
perhaps to be entirely convincing) it follows that
there may be no essential difference between the
kinds of genes in question.

In the third place it is possible that some or even
many of the commonly observed mutant genes represent degradation products of the old genes (that
is, simpler chemical bodies) that are more frequently
produced than more complex bodies. Even if this is
true it does not follow that more complex genes may
not also arise by mutation and some of these might
be dominants to the old gene. At present, however,
this is purely speculative.

In the fourth place it is known that new dominant genes do arise. There need be no necessary relation between the dominance of a gene and an

increase in the character affected. In fact, while some dominant mutants add something to the original character (size or complexity), others diminish the same character.

In the fifth place it is possible that under natural conditions dominant advantageous characters have a far better chance to become established than recessive advantageous characters, because, by definition, they produce a greater or less effect on the hybrid and give it an advantage from the start. Tempting as is such a suggestion, it would be hazardous at present to use it to explain the observed dominance of many of the characters of the wild types as compared with the recessiveness of many of the new mutant types that appear or are preserved under cultivation.

CHAPTER XII

THE NON-INHERITANCE OF ACQUIRED CHARACTERS[1]

FOR more than a hundred years the question has been discussed as to whether habits and physical characteristics acquired by an individual during its life are transmitted to its children. Lamarck's theory of evolution rests on the assumption that adaptations in the animal kingdom are brought about in this way. Although Darwin once referred contemptuously to Lamarck's nonsense, which he understood to imply that adaptation results from the slow willing of animals, he later accepted a view that is in all essential respects really the same as Lamarck's. In fact, Darwin went even further than Lamarck in attempting to explain by means of his hypothesis of pangenesis how changes in the body might be transmitted to the reproductive cells and reappear in the offspring.

Despite the high authority of Darwin's name there has been a steady falling away from this belief among biologists trained in modern methods of experimental research. It is true that among stock breeders and farmers there has always been, and there is still, a widespread conviction that acquired

[1] From The Yale Review, July 1924.

characters are transmitted, and in the folklore, both ancient and modern, of many peoples there are myths that turn on a belief in the inheritance of such characters. Phaëthon driving the chariot of the sun over Africa lost control of his father's horses and coming too near the earth, "it is said the people of Aethiopia became black because the blood was called by the heat too suddenly to surface," and they are black to this day.

The palaeontologist Cope, an ardent Lamarckian, relates a story "from that keen observer" Professor Eugene W. Hilgard, describing the origin of the twisted tails of the cats in his neighborhood. A female ("and very prolific") cat when half-grown met with an accident that produced a compound fracture. Her kittens inherited the maternal twist and found favor in the eyes of their master, described as "my Chinaman." Cope also relates the following anecdote on the authority of an educated and reliable breeder of game fowls: "A game-cock, in his second year, lost an eye in a fight. Soon after, and while the wound was very malignant (it never entirely healed), he was turned into a flock of game hens of another strain. He was otherwise healthy and vigorous. A very large proportion of his progeny has the corresponding eye defective. . . . The hens afterwards produced normal chickens with another cock. Both strains had been purely bred for ten or more years,

and none of the fowls has been blind unless from
fights."

The myths relating to prenatal impressions are
the most pathetic of all the inventions of human
credulity, and they are as old and as widespread as
the inheritance myths to which they are closely related. Jacob's slippery trick with the rods will be
long remembered. "And he set the rods which he had
pilled before the flocks in the gutters in the watering
troughs when the flocks came to drink that they
should conceive when they came to drink. And the
flocks conceived before the rods and brought forth
cattle ring-streaked, speckled, and spotted." The
world is today filled with old wives' tales of prenatal influences. These mysteries, the ill-begotten
offspring of ignorance, have contributed their bane-
ful share to the social inheritance.

It is a strange commentary that, while zoologists
have never met with much success in their endeavors
to trace the origin of structural changes to the inheritance of acquired characters, numerous pro-
posals have come from physiologists and psycholo-
gists. There was some consternation in 1923 when
the great Russian physiologist, Pawlow, reported
the results of experiments that go far beyond what
most Lamarckians have dared hope. Pawlow's conclusions—and as yet we have only his conclusions—
are very surprising. They can best be given in his
own words:

The latest experiments (which are not yet finished) show that the conditional reflexes, i.e., the highest nervous activity, are inherited. At present some experiments on white mice have been completed. Conditional reflexes to electric bells are formed, so that the animals are trained to run to their feeding place on the ringing of the bell. The following results have been obtained:

The first generation of white mice required three hundred lessons. Three hundred times was it necessary to combine the feeding of the mice with the ringing of the bell in order to accustom them to run to the feeding place on hearing the bell ring. The second generation required, for the same result, only one hundred lessons. The third generation learned to do it after thirty lessons. The fourth generation required only ten lessons. The last generation which I saw before leaving Petrograd learned the lesson after five repetitions. The sixth generation will be tested after my return. I think it very probable that after some time a new generation of mice will run to the feeding place on hearing the bell with no previous lesson.

Until we have a full account of Pawlow's methods it may be safer to wait before interpreting his results; but this is by no means a new topic, for already the effects of training and its possible inheritance had been examined by three American investigators who used the most approved methods that experience has taught are essential in obtaining data

of this sort. Miss Vicari[2] has carried out for two
years a careful set of experiments with mice, extending over four generations. The records of each individual and its pedigree were kept. The outcome
shows that no such effects as those reported by Pawlow appeared. MacDowell[3] also carried out at Cold
Spring Harbor extensive experiments on the possible effects of alcohol in inheritance as tested by ability
to learn a maze, and, as a control, kept records of
related rats that had been trained by the same tests
used for the alcoholics. His data, recently published,
show no improvement in the offspring of trained
individuals over those not trained. Halsey Bagg[4] has
published significant data on mice tested in a maze,
data that cover three generations, and here too there
is no evidence of improvement resulting from
training.

It may be objected that the methods employed
were not the same as those used by Pawlow, and,
that we must wait for his evidence. This is not to be
denied; but, on the other hand, the American data
warn us not to generalize as to the inheritance of
training. Our human experience, too, teaches cau-
tion; for how simple would our educational questions
become if our children at the sound of the school bell
learned their lessons in half the time their parents

[2] *Science,* Vol. LIX, 1924, p. 303.
[3] *Science,* Vol. LIX, 1924, p. 302.
[4] *Archives of Psychology,* Vol. XXVI, 1920.

required! We might soon look forward to the day when the ringing of bells would endow our great grandchildren with all the experiences of the generations that had preceded them.

The attempt to identify heredity with memory has been made over and over again. The most brilliant and irresponsible undertaking of this kind was that of Samuel Butler in his books on *Life and Habit* and on *Unconscious Memory*. His contention was, however, neither the first suggestion of the sort, nor was it to be the last. A few years before him a German physiologist, Hering, had elaborated this idea. Today this question has more than an historical interest, since the memory-heredity theory has never been without an advocate. Books continue to be written about it. Orr in this country advocated something of the kind, but was rather vague in his applications. Semon in Germany invented a full terminology, for his *Mneme*. Rignano in Italy attempted to give it a more physical expression, as indeed had Haeckel much earlier. Ward in England has spoken as a philosopher in its favor, and Bernard Shaw as a dramatist.

The comparison between heredity and memory has taken protean forms; none of its advocates being able to do more than throw out suggestions as to what sort of "identity" they were talking about. Fantasy rather than prosaic science is the characteristic feature of all these theories.

That these speculations have produced almost no effect on present biological thought is not surprising, for a moment's consideration will show that, at best, the basis for the comparison between memory and heredity rests only on a vague analogy. In each case something appears and reappears. In the one case, a memory of the past in the brain as we say; in the other case, a repetition of a similar type of behavior in successive generations. It is tacitly implied that because memory is a familiar process to us we must know more about it than about heredity. The fact, however, is that memory is one of the many obscure fields of human psychology. It is today more obscure to us than is heredity itself. Are we not justified, therefore, in looking askance at attempts to account for a phenomenon taking place in one realm of observation by an appeal to another, less well understood? It is not an exaggeration to say that some of those who have propounded memory theories of heredity have never been in close touch with the facts of heredity and development that are familiar to students of these subjects. Our present knowledge of the relations of parent to offspring is so different from anything ever imagined by the memory advocates, that their speculations appear to the zoologist as crude as they are often grotesque.

During the last quarter of the last century, one of the most important branches of biology came to fruition. The microscopic study of cells and eggs and their relation to development and inheritance, made great advances and cleared up many obscure questions. These observations were carried out in complete independence of the speculations concerning heredity that had gone before; and the outcome has furnished a starting point for further interpretations that have led in our own time to far reaching discoveries. It is not possible to give here even a summary of the evidence, because its understanding requires familiarity with microscopic observations covering a very wide and unfamiliar field. But, in general, I may state that the work has led to the conclusion that the properties of the reproductive cells which are responsible for the characters of the body, are inherent in these cells; and that the transmission of these properties is independent of the body-cells, and calls for no interference from them. This is summed up in the phrase "the isolation of the germ-plasm." The principal idea that this familiar phrase is intended to convey is exactly the opposite of that implied in the inheritance of acquired characters. The individual starts as an egg which is itself a cell. The egg divides and produces a vast number of cells essentially like itself. Most of these cells become changed, as development proceeds, into the tissues and organs of the body, but a few of them remain as the reproductive cells of the individual in which they live. Here they multiply to become each in turn the beginning of a new individual with its contained eggs. In a word, the egg produces the body—not the body the egg.

All this is now conceded by everyone familiar with the evidence; but two further points are open to discussion. The first of these involves the possibility that the germ-cells may be affected by the vicissitudes of the body-cells, so that when their turn comes to produce a new individual they reflect in some way the changes that have been impressed on the body-cells. If this takes place, the inheritance of acquired characters would not be incompatible with the cell theory although extraneous to the theory. The second point relates to the possibility that the changes in the external world that affect the body may produce a corresponding change in the germ-cells. No amount of argument or *a priori* reasoning is likely to settle these problems; but fortunately there is at the present time a large body of evidence, and some of it experimental evidence, that is significant, and, I think, convincing. Here, if anywhere, we may hope to find proof on which to base a reasonable judgment of the situation. To this evidence, then, I propose to appeal.

The evidence is of various sorts, and may be roughly grouped under several headings. First, that of the supposed inheritance of use and disuse. This takes us back to Lamarck, but while he rested his case on generalities that were often fantastic, such as the origin of the giraffe's long neck, there is now a

good deal of evidence that is significant and unfavorable. Darwin explained the eyeless condition
of many cave animals as a result of disuse. Recently
Payne has bred fifty generations of flies in total
darkness and has found that their reaction to light
had been in no way impaired. Darwin suggested that
the wingless condition of some insects living on
islands was due in part to disuse. Now, there have
appeared in our laboratory cultures of flies raised
in milk bottles, of three different kinds having no
wings. These appeared as single individuals with the
wings entirely absent, from parents whose wings
had not decreased visibly in size in their long confinement. Each of the new types arose by a mutation; and the inheritance of the wingless condition
shows that they owe their peculiarity to a change in
a single hereditary element, and are, in this respect,
comparable to the four hundred other mutant types
that have also arisen, whose new characters have no
conceivable relation to their confinement.

It is more difficult to obtain definite information
as to whether or not the use of a part that increases
its size or improves its functions is inherited. Imaginary cases of this sort are abundant, but since
other explanations will cover them they do not serve
our present purposes. There are no measurements,
so far as I know, to prove or to disprove the claim
that the children of blacksmiths have stronger arms

than other children, or that the children of football players have bigger legs.

William Brewer supposed that the speed of trotting horses was due chiefly "to better training but also in part to special exercise of function." Later Caspar Redfield insisted that the wisest sons have been born to the more aged fathers, and that the records of racing horses show that the fastest colts have come from parents that have been trained for racing; but his statistics will not stand the scrutiny of an actuary. Pearl has shown the fallacies that lie concealed in his premises.

The loss of a part is supposed in popular traditions to lead sometimes to its absence in the offspring. The typical example is that of the cat whose tail was pinched off by a closing door. Her kittens were tailless. There are, I believe, authentic cases of this sort, but it is also true that unpinched cats often have tailless kittens. In fact there is a special breed of these cats which when crossed to other cats transmit their peculiarity, and since from the nature of things the paternity of cats in general is always open to suspicion no great weight is to be attached to an occasional accident and the occurrence of tailless kittens—except in so far as it illustrates a curious faculty of the human mind to draw premature inferences. In rebuttal to the cat anecdotes it should be pointed out that some races of dogs and sheep have had their tails removed for generations and that puppies and lambs are born still with tails. Both Cope and Weismann cut off the tails of mice for several generations without producing bobtailed mice. We do not have to go to the lower animals to get evidence. The several kinds of mutilations and removals that man has practised on his own body for centuries have left no permanent record on the race.

From removals to distortions is a distinct step, since it has been said by some of the Lamarckians when pressed for evidence of the inheritance of loss of parts, that, after all, the part is gone, and could not be supposed to transmit its absence. This evasion does not cover the case when a distortion is in question. The stock case is the flat fish, which, according to Cunningham, owes its asymmetry to the habits acquired by its ancestors that came to lie on their sides at the bottom of the sea. One eye was thereby put out of commission, but, as a result of the muscles pulling it over so that it could peep around the corner of its own head and look up, the eye slowly shifted "in time" until today it too lies on the side of the head that is uppermost—otherwise, of course, it would have been expected to degenerate.

We do not have to go to Eocene times for evidence. Chinese women of high caste have had their feet bound and deformed for many generations, and now that the custom is being abandoned the children do not appear to have feet different from those of other Chinamen. Nearer home we do not observe the effects of the corsets of our grandmothers on the size of the waists of our children.

Several years ago a famous French physiologist, Brown-Séquard, described some interesting facts about epilepsy and malformations in guinea pigs that he interpreted as due to the inherited effects of surgical operations. At the time, these experiments aroused great interest, and were much discussed, by zoologists at least. The operations have been repeated on rather a large scale and offspring obtained, but with results so inconclusive that Séquard's work is largely forgotten, and not often quoted by those who themselves have new claims to bring to the attention of the public.

If we turn now to the experimental evidence of more recent date, we shall find several instances where induced changes have led to deformities and malformations which may "reappear" in the next generation, and hence may be said, in a sense, to be inherited. But the story they tell leads to a very different interpretation from the popular one of the inheritance of acquired character; and while it is not entirely clear sailing, yet the general trend of the work is instructive and furnishes, I think, more than a hint as to the way in which some of these results may have been produced.

I refer to the experiments of Stockard on the influence of alcohol, of Guyer on the influence of anti-

lens serum; of Griffith and Detlefsen on the effects
of long continued rotation; of Bagg and Hanson
and Little on some of the effects of radium and of
X-rays. To give a fair treatment of the interesting
results that have come out of this work would require a detailed account of the special conditions
involved in each case. To make a generalized statement that would cover them all would undoubtedly
mislead the reader. I shall attempt, therefore, a compromise between these extremes.

Many of the facts can be accounted for on the
view that the reproductive cells have been directly
injured by the treatment, and since there is evidence
that the chromosome mechanism is the basis for the
transmission of the hereditary elements, one may
even go further and suggest that the chromosomes
have been altered. Now, embryologists have been
familiar for a good many years with the injurious
effect of alcohol, of X-rays, and of radium on the
chromosomes in causing irregularities in their distribution, and with the consequent injurious effects
on the developing embryo, so that one need not go
far afield to find evidence in support of the view that
injuries produced on the germ-cell may affect the
individual that comes from it. How far the injuries
induced by these agents are specific, and how far
general is difficult to state at present; but since, as
Stockard has pointed out, the organs affected are

just those that are most subject to injury when eggs
are treated by many kinds of reagents it appears
that the results are general rather than specific. The
organs affected are the most delicate parts or the
parts that require in their development the most perfect adjustments. I am also inclined to favor such a
view, which, if established, may explain why alcohol,
and X-rays, and radium show their effects most
often in the malformations of the eye.

The more difficult task remains to attempt to ap-
praise those results in which a highly specific effect
is claimed to have been produced. Guyer's experiment easily comes first in this respect. He removed
the lenses from the eyes of rabbits, crushed them, and
injected the mash into fowls. After a time the blood
of these birds was injected into pregnant rabbits.
The lenses of the offspring were often opaque and
other abnormalities also appeared in their eyes. The
effects were transmitted to later generations both in
the male and female line. Here we have apparently
a straightforward case of specific inheritance, unless,
indeed, the injected serum is supposed to have affected not only the eyes of the embryo but their
germ-cells also. Crucial experiments would settle
this point, but as yet they have not been forthcom-
ing. Guyer's experiment has been recently repeated
by Finley and also by Huxley and Carr-Saunders
with entirely negative results. We can safely wait,

therefore, until further and more critical evidence is obtained as to the nature of the effect, if any, that was induced in Guyer's experiment.

The next best case is that of Griffith and Detlefsen. Rats were rotated for several months in cages. Some of the young born outside the cage showed irregularities in their gait, and when tested gave a different and specific response according to whether their parents had been rotated to the right or to the left. Detlefsen states that the disequilibrated rats showed frequent pathological sequelae, such as discharges from the ears; and this, he says, raises the question "whether Griffith has not merely presented us with numerous specimens of some vertebral disease." The disease once begun might be contagious, but he adds, "It is difficult to compromise this hypothesis with Griffith's contention of specificity."

This brings us finally to a point where something more definite may be said and therefore said briefly. Blakeslee and Belling have shown that if, during the maturing of the reproductive cells of a flowering plant, the common jimson weed, the plant is subjected to cold, the germ-cells may be so affected that the distribution of the chromosomes is on rare occasions altered, and a plant may be produced that has double the normal number of chromosomes. This change carries in its wake some corresponding changes of character. Changes of both these kinds often take place when the egg is not treated, and they are transmitted in the same way, so that, at best, the special environment inducing them can only be said to make their occurrence more frequent.

Finally there is a considerable body of evidence showing that characters, whose development is known to be affected by environmental influences (which therefore might be supposed to be the very best kind of material to exhibit the effect of acquired characters) are not affected by the changes induced in their parents by the environment. There are several striking cases of this kind that have been met with in the course of our experiments with vinegar flies. There is a race of these flies that have been long inbred, in order to make them uniform in a genetic sense, in which the eyes are entirely absent in most individuals, but occasionally one or both eyes may be present much reduced in size. If the flies that have these small eyes are bred to each other they give exactly the same results as when their eyeless brothers and sisters are bred together. As each stock culture gets older, more and more of the flies that emerge have eyes, and, towards the end, an increased number of the flies have both eyes present and almost full size. If some of these are used as the parents of a new generation, the results obtained are precisely the same as when eyeless flies are used. What better evidence could we hope to obtain to show that the presence of a character in the individual has no influence on the reproductive cells? This case does not stand alone but is duplicated by similar evidence from other characters subject to environmental changes in these flies, namely, bar eyes, abnormal abdomen, and extra legs, all of which are greatly affected by the environment, but the effects are not transmitted. Is it surprising, then, in the light of these detailed and controlled data that we should look askance at claims which pretend to demonstrate the inheritance of acquired characters from observations that are in most cases inadequate to prove the point at issue?

The experiments that Kammerer has carried on for several years relate, for the most part, to the kind of characters which I have just mentioned. He finds that salamanders spotted with black and yellow change to more black or more yellow individuals if kept on a black or a yellow background. Their offspring reared on a neutral background show, he believes, some influence of the effects produced on their parents, and so on. Until these results are repeated on material that is more thoroughly controlled, or on material where the effect produced can be stated in measurable terms and not by pictures of selected material, it is in my opinion better to suspend judgment in respect to their interpretation. The careful work of Herbst that was undertaken to check up Kammerer's evidence has so far found no justification for Kammerer's conclusion. Much of the other work that Kammerer has brought forward as evidence of the inherited effect of the environment is open to the same objection—the inheritance of color changes in lizards, the change in the breeding habits of the midwife toad, and the development of horny pads on the thumbs of the male. That the environment causes changes in some of these characters need not be questioned, but that the effects produced are transmitted to the next generation, through the bodily changes produced, may be questioned, both because of the inadequacy of the evidence and also because in other cases where the materials are suitable for making such tests there is no evidence that such influences produce such results. Perhaps the most careful and thoughtful piece of analytical work that has been done in this field is that by Sumner, extending over five years, on the effect of heat and cold on the length of the tail, ears, and feet of white mice, as well as on the increase in the thickness of the hair in the cold.

Some of the mice were reared from birth in a cold room, others in a warm room. The average difference in temperature was eighteen degrees centigrade. The tails of the mice in the warm room series were longer than the tails of those in the cold, for mice of the same body length. The length of the feet and of the ears was also greater in the warmer room, although the effect of the cold on the ears was inconstant. These two kinds of mice were then brought together in a common room of intermediate temperature, where each series was bred separately, and measurements were made of the offspring when the mice were full grown. It was found that the tail, foot, and ear length were greater in the mice of warm-room parentage than that of cold-room parentage but the difference was not so great as that between their parents.

This may be interpreted to mean that the smaller increase shown by the tails of these mice of the second generation from warm-room parents was due to the intermediate temperature in which they were reared, while their length, which was greater than that of the mice of cold-room parentage, was inherited from the warm-room parents. But how? Was it the effect of cold on the germ-cells, or did it come from the longer tails of their parents? It is not easy to imagine that the effect was due to the direct influence of the cold on the germ-cells since mice are warm blooded and maintain a nearly constant body temperature when adult, and as young mice they were kept warm in the nest and by the brooding of their mothers. Must we then conclude that the germ-cells are so sensitive to slight differences in the size of the organs of the body that the effects are shown in the next generation? If so, might we not expect that all individual differences would reappear in the characters of the offspring?

But this question, at least, has now been settled by Johannsen's brilliant analysis on the non-inheritance of individual differences that are called forth by the environment. His experiments were carried out on material that was adequate to give a crucial answer to the question involved. In support of Johannsen's conclusion there is an extensive body of genetic evidence which can be interpreted as meaning that while much individual variability is due to minor genetic factors, and this is inherited, some individual variability is due to the environment and this is not inherited.

Is it possible, then, that Sumner's results were due to chance, in the sense that the two series happened to give the averages shown? It does not seem probable that this was so, but we can never be certain until the experiment is repeated on material that is first made pure for factors involving the length of the parts to be studied. Sumner is himself very cautious in his interpretation of his results. He says, "At no time have I declared my results to be proof of, or even evidence for, the inheritance of acquired characters. Indeed, I have insisted that in the present state of our problems this latter expression has become hopelessly obsolete. As regards the various possible interpretations of my own results I have always expressed indecision."

Castle and Phillips performed an experiment on guinea pigs that would be expected to show the influence of the body on the germ-cells if such effects are possible. The ovary from a black female was transplanted into a white female whose ovary had been removed. After the transplanted ovary had established itself, the white female was bred to a pure white male. The offspring were black, although the mother and the father were white. The eggs had not been affected by their sojourn in the body of a white individual.

It is not as widely known as it should be that most of the assumptions of the Lamarckians contradict·the fundamental principles of Mendel's law of heredity. Mendel's law of segregation states that the hereditary elements received from the parents separate in the germ-cells of the offspring without having affected each other, and, by implication, without having been affected by the character of the individual in which they were contained. An example will make this statement clearer. Suppose a white mouse is bred to a wild gray mouse. The hybrid offspring will be gray. If two such hybrids are bred together they give rise to gray and to white offspring in the ratio of three grays to one white. This ratio is understandable if in the hybrids half of the reproductive cells carry the element for gray and half that for white. Thousands of instances of this sort are known today. To reject the evidence would be scientific suicide; to refuse to accept the theory would be to throw reason to the winds. Mendel's postulates concerning the clear separation of the elements of heredity mean that the white-producing elements in the gray hybrids have been unaffected by the gray color of the hair of the animal that carries them.

Many similar types of inheritance in man tell the same story. A blue-eyed man marries a brown-eyed woman, and if she has come from a race pure for brown eyes, all the children will have brown eyes. If an individual of this parentage marries another with a similar parentage their children will be brown-eyed and blue-eyed as three to one. Still another case may seem more impressive since the character involved is one that dominates the normal and may appear therefore as something more positive in its nature. There is a type of malformed hand in which the middle segment of each finger is missing. If a short-fingered man marries a normal handed woman half of the children will have short-fingered hands and half of them will be normal. The explanation here is the same as before. The man was a hybrid (his father had short fingers and his mother was normal), hence he produces two kinds of reproductive cells. When he marries a woman whose reproductive cells are normal, two kinds of offspring are expected and two kinds are found. It may be added that the normal children show no trace whatsoever of the influence of the hand of their short-fingered father and never transmit this deformity to their descendants—the separation of the elements in the dominant parent has been clean.

It is scarcely necessary to elaborate this theme.
The facts are not disputed by any student of genetics who is familiar with the evidence; and they furnish, in my judgment, convincing disproof of the
loose and vague arguments of the Lamarckians.

The "will to believe" in the inheritance of acquired characters is widespread and an interesting
feature of human behavior. The eagerness with
which each new claim is listened to is only too familiar to those who concern themselves with evolutionary controversies.

The willingness to listen to every new tale that
furnishes evidence of the inheritance of acquired
characters arises perhaps from a human longing to
pass on to our offspring the fruits of our bodily
gains and mental accumulations. While every scientific investigator has sympathy for this human weakness, he cannot allow it to influence him in his examination of the facts as they actually exist. In our
hope for the best we forget that we are invoking a
principle that also calls for the inheritance of the
worst. If we cannot inherit the effects of the training of our parents, we escape at least the inheritance
of their misfortunes. A receptive mind may be a
better asset for the child than a mind weighted down
from birth with the successes and failures of its
ancestors.

Chapter XIII

HUMAN INHERITANCE

A LARGE number of malformations in man have been shown to be inherited. In the medical literature there are hundreds of family pedigrees in which one or another defect appears in successive generations, especially when the stock has been rather closely inbred, or where the defect is a dominant one. The few books in which these cases of human inheritance have been collected may give the impression that our knowledge of man's heredity is mainly concerned with the transmission of his defects. The eugenic programme or recommendations with which these treatises usually wind up may give the impression that our chief concern with human inheritance relates to the elimination of the defective materials (cacogenics) that have become incorporated in the species, rather than with the discovery of superlative human materials, their preservation and perpetuation (eugenics). All this calls for comment.

General Statement

In extenuation of the depressing effect of such literature it may be said that malformations are utilized for genetic work not because of their intrinsic interest—although to the pathologist they are in themselves important—but because, as in other species, they furnish clear-cut characters that are sharply separated from normal structures, and hence can be traced through successive generations. It may properly be claimed that in studying the inheritance of each defect we are also studying the inheritance of a normal character that forms the other member of the contrasted pair. This statement, however, calls for an important reservation; for, all that we mean by such a contrast is that the "normal" is not the abnormal. We do not in reality know anything more than this. This relation is, however, inherent in all Mendelian contrasted character-pairs, unless members of an allelomorphic series are somewhat more specific.

The presence of malformations of the body in human stocks is not supposed to be due to a greater tendency in the human species than in other species to produce, *de novo,* defective mutants, but rather to be due in man to the preservation of individuals having such characters and allowing them to marry, or at least not preventing them from mating. The higher ethical standards of man lead him to preserve human life, and in the absence of severe competition (through which the maladjusted would go under) the defective child reaches maturity.

If the new character is recessive its gene may become widely disseminated in the human germ-material before two individuals each with the recessive gene mate. One-fourth of their offspring will then show the defect. By the time this has occurred the gene may have become so widely spread that the most that can be done—if something is to be done— is to discourage the defective individuals that have reappeared from further contamination—a council of perfection that may not be appreciated.

When the defect is dominant it will appear in half the offspring[1] if marriage with a normal person occurs. The other half of the children that are normal do not transmit this dominant defect, and have, so to speak, escaped entirely from the inheritance.

There are, however, a number of cases where the defect is not perfectly dominant. This means that its variability is so wide that a few individuals that carry the gene may fail to show it, or show it to such a small degree as to escape casual examination. There are, apparently, cases of this sort which have been utilized by the opponents of the modern theory of heredity as justification for the statement that such a character does not show "strictly Mendelian inheritance." Unless suitable tests are made it is not possible to claim that extreme cases of this sort are exceptions to Mendelian inheritance, for, similar cases are known in other animals, and have been shown not to be exceptions, but due to the wide variability of the hybrid character.

Aside from the major physical defects there are many smaller ones that do not interfere seriously

[1] Assuming the parent is heterozygous for the character.

with the welfare of the individual, or which can be corrected by modern appliances or operations. We have far less information concerning the inheritance of these blemishes, and at present can seldom be certain that they are inherited or how they are inherited. Only by comparison with the better-known cases can we surmise that inheritance may play a rôle in many of them. Since the disadvantages that follow are slight, or can be corrected, these defects have little practical importance, which need not, however, detract from their theoretical interest. Other ways than elimination by means of artificial selection have been found to standardize individuals that show these slight departures. Corrective surgery has proven a more efficacious remedy in man than the slow process of selective breeding.

In genetic work each mutant type (defective or otherwise) is contrasted with the original type from which it came, sometimes called the normal type. In man and in some of the domesticated animals there is no standard or original type with which to make such a comparison; and opinions may even differ as to what is to be regarded as a normal type, each race having probably a standard of its own. The situation is the same in several domestic races of animals and garden plants. In some, the new mutant genes have entirely replaced the original genes, i.e., the race has become pure for certain mutant genes. Whenever the original genes have been replaced by mutant genes it is not possible to recover the old type, but if two races have independently arisen from the same original wild type, and have accumulated different sets of mutant genes, it is still possible to obtain the original type by crossing in so far as each has retained some of the original genes. For example, there are two white breeds of fowls which when crossed produce offspring showing the colored plumage of the wild jungle fowl. Similarly there are two white races of sweet peas which if crossed give the color of the purple Sicilian wild pea from which our cultivated forms are said to have come. Some of the races of mankind have been long separated. It might seem possible to recover the type from which they have departed by crossing them. Racial crosses have been made frequently, and the hybrids described, but there is no way of determining how far the outcome represents in certain respects the common ancestral type, and how far it is due to the interacting dominant factors of the combination. Possibly it might be supposed that the mulatto, with a yellow skin, that results from the white-negro cross represents the type of skin color from which both white and the negro races have diverged. If so, a yellow race breeding true to that color might be obtained after the white and the black genes had been replaced by the original yellow genes. As yet there is no certain record of such a consummation, although the deficiency of white-skinned and black-skinned offspring from mulattos of later generations might in some few cases be accounted for in this way. On the other hand the intermediate color of the mulatto of the first generation might be due to the interaction of the incompletely dominant genes of the two parents, and in later generations it might not be possible to distinguish by inspection alone such a condition from that due to the restoration of the original normal genes. It would require elaborate genetic tests to settle such a question.

Meanwhile we shall have to rest content with the admission that there is no single type of human normal individual with which to standardize the different racial types. At best, cases of human atavism produced by crossing, would be expected to go no further back than the race to which the modern types of men converge, and from an evolutionary point of view this is a very recent event. We should anticipate, therefore, that all the races of mankind have an enormous number of genes in common and only few that are different. The latter produce the relatively slight structural differences that are found in different races.

The Inheritance of Physical Defects

A few examples of the inheritance of physical characters in man will suffice to show that in his inheritance man conforms to the same laws that regulate the inheritance of other animals and plants.

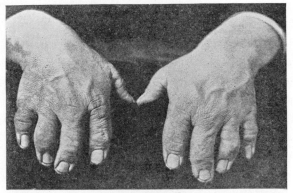

Fig. 65.—Two Brachydactyl hands. (*After Farabee.*)

Fig. 66.—An X-ray photo-
graph of the bones of a
Brachydactyl hand.

There is a rare abnormality of the hand and foot
known as brachydactyly, or short-fingeredness (*figs.*
65, 66). Farabee has recorded the history of an

American family of this sort, and Drinkwater that
of a British family, and later of a second family that
migrated from America back to England. As seen
in *figure* 65, the fingers of the brachydactyl hand
are short owing to the absence of the middle segment
of each finger. The fingers are about half normal
length. A short-fingered man marrying a normal
woman transmits the defect to half of the children.
The character is dominant (*fig.* 67). There are no
recorded cases of the marriage of two short-fingered
persons and the pure (or double) dominant character is unknown. There is a possibility that such an
individual might not be viable.

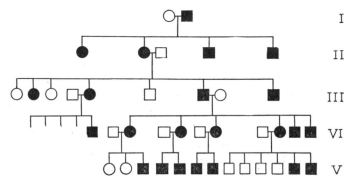

Fɪɢ. 67.—Pedigree chart of the inheritance of Brachydactyly.
(*After Farabee.*)

Drinkwater has also recorded other cases of *minor*
brachydactyly in which the fingers are less shortened. Several other cases in which one or more of

the fingers are short have been described. One such case—also a dominant—has been traced by Mohr and Wriedt through six generations which carries the pedigree to the year 1764. Here the shortening involves mainly the forefinger (*fig.* 68).

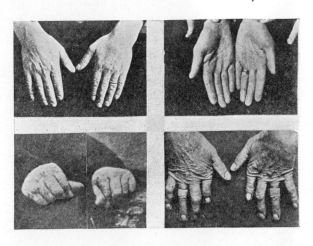

Fig. 68.—Four pairs of hands showing a shortened condition of the fore-finger. (*After Mohr and Wriedt.*)

Color-blindness is a sex-linked recessive character in man. A color-blind man married to a normal woman has only normal daughters and sons; all of the daughters, however, transmit color-blindness to half of their sons (*fig.* 69).

Color-blind women are rare, because they can never arise unless a color-blind man marries a woman who is color-blind, or else marries a normal woman who had a color-blind father, or had a mother heterozygous for color-blindness (*fig.* 70).

The pedigrees of color-blind families—and they are many—leave little doubt as to the mode of inheritance of this character (*fig.* 71).

Accepting this evidence as on the whole satisfac-

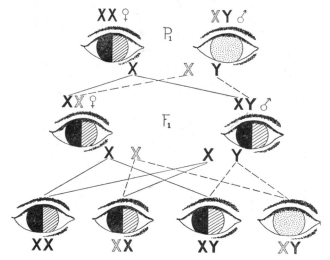

F$_{IG}$. 69.—Diagram to show the inheritance of color-blindness in man. The eye that can distinguish red from green is here half black, half barred, while the color-blind eye is stippled. A color-blind man mates with a normal woman. The sons and daughters are normal. Two individuals of such parentage give three normals to one color-blind individual in F_2. The color-blind individual is always a male.

tory, there is still something more to be said. As is well known, there are many grades of color-blindness. We do not know whether these grades are due to individual, non-genetic, variations—assuming it to be due to one gene; or whether there are several genes that differ in the degree to which they produce the defect. We know of a good many cases in other animals where there are several mutations of the same gene. For instance, in Drosophila there is a

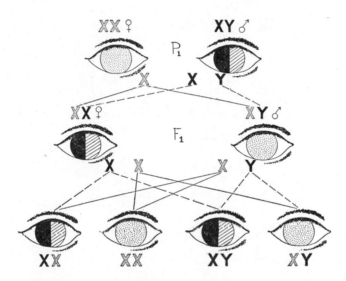

F IG . 70.—The designations as in *fig.* 69. Here a color-blind woman mates with a normal male. All of her sons are color-blind, her daughters have normal vision (but carry a factor for color-blindness). In the F_2 generation, half the daughters and half the sons have normal eyes and half are color-blind.

series of ten such multiple allelomorphs for eye colors that range from pure white to deep wine-red.

There is still another possible interpretation of the different kinds of color-blindness—one which *a priori* would seem to be the most probable—

namely, that the differences are due to other modifying genes that affect the extent to which the
character develops.

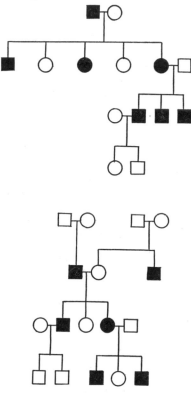

Fig. 71.—Two pedigrees for color-
blindness. (*After Lenz.*)

Blue eyes in man behaves as a recessive to brown
eyes. Two blue-eyed parents have only blue-eyed
children (*fig. 72*). Pure brown-eyed individuals

have only brown-eyed children (*fig. 72*), but a
brown-eyed individual, one of whose parents had
blue eyes, married to a blue-eyed individual has both
blue- and brown-eyed children in equal numbers according to Mendelian expectation. In recent years a

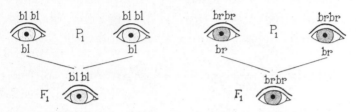

Fig. 72.—Diagram to illustrate the inheritance of blue eyes (to
the left), and of brown eyes (to the right).

few cases have been recorded where two blue-eyed
parents have had some brown-eyed children, and
this has furnished the opponents of Mendelian
inheritance with an argument against the general
application of Mendel's theory. Such cases are, however, only an argument against an overstatement
of that theory as always applying to apparently
blue-eyed individuals. It is known that occasionally
blue-eyed individuals have only a speck of brown
pigment in their eyes. They may then produce some
brown-eyed children. In other words, the hybrid
brown eye-color is variable in extent, and at one extreme shows almost no brown color or possibly none
at all, and yet is genetically brown-eyed. That this
is the true explanation is shown by the pedigree of

these genetic browns, for, so far as recorded they have had at least one brown-eyed parent. In other words, in extreme and exceptional cases possibly due to weakness or disease the brown eye-color may not develop in an individual that is genetically a brown hybrid. This failure of the somatic character does not affect the brown-producing gene, for, such individuals behave in inheritance as hybrid brown-eyed individuals.

Albinism in man has been known for a long time and the earlier records of white Indians seem, in the light of recent discoveries, not to be mythical. In all races, including negros, albinos are known. It has been estimated that this occurs once in 5,000 to once in 30,000 individuals. It is possible that there is more than a single kind of albino due to mutation in different genes or to allelomorphic mutations that give different degrees of deficiency of pigment.

Albinism is a recessive character. A few cases are on record where two albinos have had only albino children. In true albinos the brown pigment is absent from the skin, hair, and iris. Its absence in the iris gives the eye a pink color due to the blood in the back of the eye, showing through the semi-transparent iris.

A defect in vision known as stationary night-blindness has been shown by Nettleship to be a dominant Mendelian trait (*fig.* 73). In one locality

(near Montpellier in France) it has been traced to
the year 1637 and hence has been handed down for
about two hundred and fifty years. There are other
types of night-blindness that have a different inheritance not entirely made out.

Haemophilia in man has been shown to be trans-

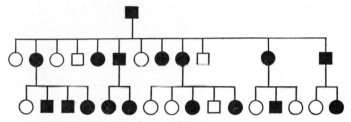

FIG. 73.—Diagram to show the inheritance of night-blindness.
(*After Nettleship.*)

mitted as a sex-linked character (*fig. 74*). The blood
of affected individuals fails to coagulate quickly
when exposed to air, hence there is danger of the
individual bleeding to death. Several pedigrees have
been made out. It is a recessive character whose gene
is carried by the X-chromosome. It appears in any
male whose single X-chromosome carries the gene
for haemophilia. Its relative infrequency in women
is explained on the grounds that it can appear in
them only when the father and mother both possess
the character or when the mother herself has had a
haemophilic father—in other words when both X-
chromosomes carry the gene.

The Four Blood Groups and their Inheritance

One of the most remarkable cases of heredity in man is found in the so-called blood groups. As first shown by Von Dungern and Hirschfeld in 1910 the inheritance of the four blood groups conforms to

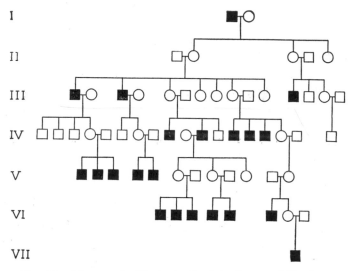

FIG. 74.—Diagram to illustrate the inheritance of bleeding or haemophilia. (*After Bulloch and Fildes.*)

Mendel's laws. So consistent is this relation that, as Ottenberg pointed out in 1921, the evidence might be used in certain cases to determine the parentage of the child. The presence of two pairs of factors will account for the results. Thus if one pair of genes be represented by *A* and *a* and the other pair by *B* and *b*, and if an individual with the genetic constitution *AaBb* be mated to another individual of like constitution (*AaBb*), then each will contain four kinds of germ cells, viz., *AB, Ab, Ba,* and *ab.* The sixteen possible combinations formed, if any sperm may fertilize any egg, are shown in *figure 75.*

These sixteen individuals fall into four groups according to whether they have both *A* and *B*, or

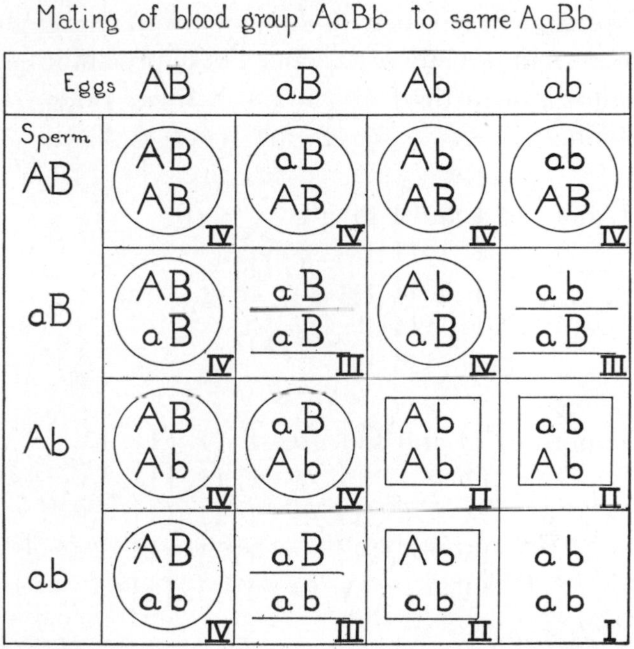

Fig. 75.—Diagram illustrating the sixteen classes of individuals when two members of the blood group *AaBa* mate. There are four classes of individuals produced, indicated by the circles, lines, squares, and absence of *A* and *B*.

only *A,* or only *B,* or neither *A* nor *B* (i.e., *ab*) in the proportion of 9*AB*:3*A*:3*B*:1*ab*. These four genetic classes correspond to the four recognized blood types IV, II, III, I, as indicated in the diagram.

Now these sixteen kinds of individuals are found in all populations, so far studied, although in somewhat different proportions in different "races."

It is very simple to tell what the kinds of genetic offspring will be when any one of these sixteen individuals marries any other one. These possibilities are summarized in the following statement taken from Ottenberg:

Unions of I and I give I

$$\left.\begin{array}{cc} \text{I} & \text{II} \\ \text{II} & \text{II} \end{array}\right\} \text{I, II}$$

$$\left.\begin{array}{cc} \text{I} & \text{III} \\ \text{III} & \text{III} \end{array}\right\} \text{I, III}$$

Unions of II and III give		I, II, III, IV
IV	I	I, II, III, IV
IV	II	I, II, III, IV
IV	III	I, II, III, IV
IV	IV	I, II, III, IV.

Two actual pedigrees, one of them carried through three generations, will serve to illustrate particular cases (*fig. 76*).

From a knowledge of the blood group to which the child belongs it is possible to predict to what groups its parents may have belonged, and in certain cases it is possible to state that an individual of a cer-

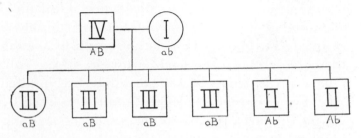

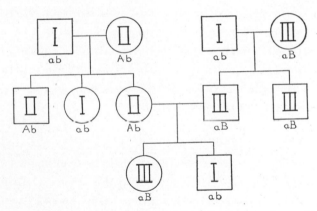

Fig. 76.—Two pedigrees showing the inheritance of two blood groups. See text.

tain group could not have been the parent of a particular child.

In the transfusion of blood from one individual

to another, that is sometimes necessary, it is essential that the blood corpuscles of the donor are not agglutinated by the serum of the recipient. Thus it is a matter of great importance to select a donor that does not bring about such a catastrophe. The simple rules are that individuals belonging to the same blood group (I, II, III, or IV) do not agglutinate each other's blood, but the blood corpuscles of an individual represented by *AA* or *Aa* will be precipitated if the donor contains the agglutinin represented by *aa*, and similarly the blood corpuscles of an individual represented by *BB* or *Bb* will be precipitated if the donor contains the agglutinin represented by *bb*. Inspection of the diagram will show that group II (with serum *bb*) precipitates III and IV, and group III (with serum *aa*) precipitates II and IV. Further, the serum of group I (*aa bb*) precipitates all of the other groups; while the serum of group IV precipitates none of the others.

Inheritance of Other Traits

There are numerous other physical characters of man that are evidently inherited but where the number of factors involved is uncertain or entirely unknown. Some of these characters are present in all races. Others to some extent are racial characters. Thus height in man is a very variable character. It is obviously a complex of several or many elements little understood. Differences in length of legs, or of body, or of neck, and of different combinations of these may be present. Height is a growth phenomenon depending amongst other things on the time at which the growth of the bones, especially the long bones of the leg, stops, and this in turn is, to some extent at least, connected with the time of sexual maturity, which depends again on the time of functioning or the amount of secretion produced by some of the glands of internal secretion (testes or ovary, thyroid, pituitary, etc.). These inter-relations have made the study of growth very difficult especially when the determination of the rate of growth or its cessation is connected with internal organs that are seldom seen or measured. Nevertheless there is nothing in these complications that precludes the possibility that the ultimate source of the variability is due to genetic factors.

There is little accurate information at present as to the number of factor differences that are involved in the inheritance of hair color in man. The changes in color that take place during the life of the individual renders its study difficult. An individual child may start with flaxen hair, later have brown hair, and in old age become white-headed. Three generations living at the same time may show these differences. A complete record would then have to extend over several years; for, hearsay evidence as to the color of the hair of the grandparent when in middle age may be inaccurate and the future color of the hair of a child would be largely guessing. Data collected by the questionnaire method, that has been used in the study of the inheritance of hair color, can not be relied upon without some more definite standard than popular designations of shades of color.

The Inheritance of Mental Traits

Man's success as a social animal depends as much on his mental qualities as on his physical characteristics. No one will deny, I suppose, that men behave in different ways, but who can say how far differences in human behavior depend on the physique of the individual, how far on his early experiences and training, and how far on differences in his sense organs and central nervous system? Until some of these questions are better understood it is impossible to know how far observed differences are innate and how far acquired.

Here again, as in the case of man's physical defects, there are a few extremely abnormal conditions where the evidence indicates that something is inherited, but even here there is much that is obscure. The case most often quoted is feeble-mindedness that has been said to be inherited as a Mendelian recessive, but until some more satisfactory definition can be given as to where feeble-mindedness begins and ends, and until it has been determined how many and what internal physical defects may produce a general condition of this sort, and until it has been determined to what extent feeble-mindedness is due to syphilis, it is extravagant to pretend to claim that there is a single Mendelian factor for this condition.

Family pedigrees in which an unusual number of individuals below par are present undoubtedly give the impression that something is inherited, but until all the social conditions surrounding the childhood of the individual are examined and given proper weight, serious doubts will arise as to what form of inheritance is producing the results. It is quite probable that there are extraneous factors involved in such pedigrees.

There is no *a priori* objection to the assumption that different sense organs and different brains react as differently as do other organs of the body. Those that react below some selected standard might be called feeble-minded; but there are no grounds for assuming that the results are due to one particular defect in the nervous system, and in fact a critical study of the cases shows that they are probably not all due to a single factor difference or even to the same ones. The pedigrees that have been published showing a long history of social misconduct, crime, alcoholism, debauchery, and venereal diseases are open to the same criticism from a genetic point of view; for it is obvious that these groups of individuals have lived under demoralizing social conditions that might swamp a family of average persons. It is not surprising that, once begun from whatever

cause, the effects may be to a large extent communi-
cated rather than inherited.

It is quite possible of course that an inherited defective dominant character might furnish the starting point for these histories, but that the subsequent
events are all due to "bad blood" or "defective germ-
plasm" remains to be shown.

"Insanity" is another "psychological trait" that
is said to be inherited and the numerous pedigrees
that have been collected showing that certain types
of insanity occur more frequently in certain fami-

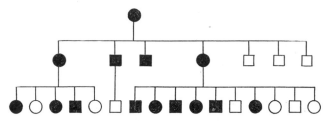

Fig. 77.—Chart showing the inheritance of Huntington's
chorea. (*After Davenport.*)

lies than in others seem to furnish evidence in support of such a claim. This is particularly the case
in Huntington's chorea (*fig. 77*) a type of insanity,
often leading ultimately to suicide, that does not
appear as a rule until middle life or later. Since it
appears to be dominant, its history is more easily
followed than in most other cases where the dominance or recessiveness is in question. Huntington's
chorea has been traced in a limited group of indi-

viduals. The background of its expression appears to be connected in some way with the sex organs but what this connection may be is unknown, for it appears in both sexes which makes it difficult to account for the disturbance on the basis of a sex endocrine.

At best one can say, perhaps, that in certain strains and perhaps under certain conditions mental disorders appear, but so long as neither the physiological background of insanity, or the external agents, that are contributory, are known, its genetic relations must remain obscure.

If these "best cases" are so far from being established on a scientific footing, it is not particularly profitable to discuss the many claims that have been set up for other mental traits, even though it must be conceded that *defective* characteristics might be the ones, judging by analogy with mutant physical defects, that would be more likely to furnish evidence of Mendelian inheritance than the less extreme differences that distinguish "normal" individuals. The important point, however, to be urged is that the "mental traits" in man are those that are most often the product of the environment which obscures to a large extent their inheritance, or at least makes very difficult their study.

While the inheritance of disorders relative to human behavior are of importance to the pathologist and to the penologist, the inheritance of individual differences that fall within what would be called the "normal" is more important from the point of view of human evolution. Here also we are on very dubious grounds when we discuss the inheritance of individual mental peculiarities, and in still greater danger of error if we attempt to discriminate between racial complexes. The similarity in behavior or in "temperament" or mental qualities of identical twins might be expected to furnish important information as to how much is acquired and how much inherited. The very close physical similarity of twins of this kind might make such material favorable for study. There are, however, even here two serious drawbacks that complicate the results. In the first place unless the twins had been separated in very early childhood it would be difficult to decide how much is due to similarity of nature and how much to nurture. A comparison with other children in the same family may be helpful but is not decisive, for the experience of each child from successive births is affected by older and younger children in the family. In the second place the so-called standard tests may measure training rather than constitutional factors. Until these difficulties can be overcome, the many anecdotes of the close similarity in temperaments, or abilities, of identical twins do not supply the needed evidence.

We can, by artificial selection, eliminate structural defects from a race of animals or plants and by proper breeding make the race more uniform and maintain it at or near a chosen standard. Since we have many good reasons to think that man's physical inheritance conforms to the same principles that apply to other animals, it follows that by elimination and suitable mating man too could be standardized. How far one might have to go in order to carry out this reformation is a matter of opinion. If too strenuous standards were set up the human race might be exterminated before the reformation began. Genetic reformers and racial propagandists do little more than recommend cutting off a few of the most defective individuals. But it is not so much the physically defective that appeal to their sympathies as the "morally" deficient and this is supposed to apply to mental traits rather than to physical characters. Ruthless genetic (?) reform here might seem too drastic and might be retroactive if pressed too far. Social reforms might, perhaps, more quickly and efficiently get at the root of a part of the trouble, and until we know how much the environment is responsible for, I am inclined to think that the student of human heredity will do well to recommend more enlightenment on the social causes of deficiencies rather than more elimination in the present deplorable state of our ignorance as to the causes of mental differences.

Lest it appear from what has been said that I have too little faith in the importance of breeding for mental superiority I should like to add that I am inclined to think that there are considerable individual differences in man that are probably strictly genetic, even though I insist that at present there is for this no real scientific evidence of the kind that we are familiar with in other animals and in plants. I will even venture to go so far as to suppose that the average of the human race might be improved by eliminating a few of the extreme disorders, however they may have arisen. In fact, this is attempted at present on a somewhat extensive scale by the segregation into asylums of the insane and feebleminded. I should hesitate to recommend the incarceration of all their relatives if the character is suspected of being recessive, or of their children if a dominant. After all, these segregations are based on humanitarian principles, or for our protection rather than for genetic reasons. How long and how extensively this casual isolation of adults would have to go on to produce any considerable decrease in defectives, no informed person would, I should think, be willing to state.

Least of all should we feel any assurance in deciding genetic superiority or inferiority as applied to whole races, by which is meant not races in a biological sense but social or political groups bound together by physical conditions, by religious sentiments, or by political organizations. The latter have their roots in the past and are acquired by each new generation as a result of imitation and training. If it is unjust "to condemn a whole *people*" meaning thereby a political group, how much more hazardous is it, as some sensational writers have not hesitated to do, to pass judgment as to the relative genetic inferiority or superiority of different *races*.

If within each human social group the geneticist finds it impossible to discover, with any reasonable certainty, the genetic basis of behavior, the problems must seem extraordinarily difficult when groups are contrasted with each other where the differences are obviously connected not only with material advantages and disadvantages resulting from location, climate, soil, and mineral wealth, but with traditions, customs, religions, taboos, conventions, and prejudices. A little goodwill might seem more fitting in treating these complicated questions than the attitude adopted by some of the modern race-propagandists.

INDEX